A STRANGER
IN PARIS

A STRANGER IN PARIS

Karen Webb

First Published 2020 by Impress Books

Impress Books, 13-14 Crook Business Centre, New Road, Crook,

County Durham, DL15 8QX

© Karen Webb 2020

The right of the author to be identified as the originator of this work has

been asserted in accordance with the Copyright,

Designs and Patents Act 1988.

British Library Cataloguing in Publication Data

A catalogue record for this book is available from the British Library.

ISBN: 978-1-911293-61-3

For Gran

Acknowledgements

With Acknowledgements to Roger Mathews, without whose patience and encouragement this book would not have been written.

To my husband William who took care of everything else, so I could write.

To Andrew Lownie who told me to put the stories on paper, and Jane Dorner on her Memoir writing course (A Chapter Away) who told me to go deeper.

To Heather Whitehall Trochon and Debbie Stocker who said 'next bit, please'.

And above all Richard Willis of Impress, who liked the story enough to take a chance.

Author's note

This book is written from memory almost thirty years after the events. Inevitably conversations are not transcripts of exact conversations and events may not always be strictly chronological. Names and identifying characteristics and details such as physical properties, occupations and places of residence have been changed so that to all intents and purposes this book may be considered a work of fiction and any resemblance to persons living or dead is entirely coincidental.

"There is never any ending to Paris and the memory of each person who has lived in it differs from that of any other ..."

Ernest Hemingway, A Moveable Feast.

CHAPTER 1

Aberystwyth, 1989

The ambitiously named 'Sprinter' wound into Aberystwyth station signalling the end of my university life. It was time to say goodbye to drenched hair, waxed raincoats and missed deadlines, never mind three years of not understanding the bottom half of municipal signposts. I was off to Paris, city of lights and romance, to be reunited with the love of my life, Monsieur David Azoulay. Standing with me on the platform to mark this momentous occasion were my closest friends of recent months – a group of men in long robes huddled against the spitting rain; their decision to don the national costume of their home countries adding a bright, if somewhat incongruous, note to the station platform. The guard threw a suspicious glance in our direction as he strolled past, blowing a sharp blast of warning into his whistle. We resembled a mislaid pantomime cast heading for Blackpool pier. Half the group were muttering in foreign languages, none of which were Welsh.

The men's grimaces and doleful looks were clear enough to decipher in any language: *You bloody idiot, are you really prepared to lose your last shred of pride? You little fool, embarking on this journey; this hiding to nothing.* In their eyes, I was a ridiculous English woman; chasing after a French man who had told me *it's over;* pursuing a man of deep faith, whose parents had torn my letters before his eyes for *he* was an Orthodox Jew and I was not.

Not that the man I had loved for the past few months had looked or dressed like an Orthodox Jew. Not, at least, when playing the field at Aberystwyth. I'd checked out stock images at the library. There'd been nothing to give away David's game. No clues in his razor-sharp hair or hound-tooth jacket. He'd whispered nothing about Judaism into my ear when we first met, only sweet nothings in that drawling French accent which had left me dribbling into my snakebite at the union bar. If there were any subtler clues, then I'd missed them! And by the time I knew what all of this meant, it was too late. I should accept my fate and see the sense of David's words. That's what Rafi said. My station friends shared strict Muslim values. They were unsympathetic to what they considered to be my borderline stalking. My chosen one would never make an honest woman of me. This was their collective belief. My market value had been lowered, in Habte's words, to less than that of a geriatric camel.

They pressed me to the centre of our group; a rogue

weed that had sprouted up between them, and the tears streamed down my cheeks as I realised that I would probably never see these men again. There had been sulking and fighting, yet they had been everything that family could be during those last months before finals. They had spent their energies attempting to exercise the control of a frustrated parent over a wayward child and I had repaid them with rebellion.

Today was the day when they would finally wash their hands of me. It had been an emotional train-wreck of a journey, but I was finally free, and my adult life could begin.

Five months earlier I hadn't a single Frenchman on my list of friends and acquaintances, let alone any intention of starting a new life with one.

It was a bleak day during the first week of January and I had returned to university after a disastrous Christmas holiday with my Welsh fiancé Steve. There was a funny postcard circulating in Aberystwyth gift shops at the time. On one side there was a sheep pelted by hailstones in the winter, and on the other a sheep pelted by hailstones in the summer – with no difference between the two. I'd long since given up trying to brush my hair straight or keep my makeup on longer than half an hour. For nearly three years I was that bedraggled creature, hair curling wildly in the damp air. I trundled my case along the pier to a line of shabby Victorian houses. My room was part of an end terrace which faced out to sea towards the war memorial. Cold and damp had blistered the gaudy pink plaster so it resembled a pock-marked diva.

Reaching my doorstep, the relief I had felt at making it home turned immediately sour when my key refused to enter the lock. I forced it, but it jammed, sticking half in, half out, the rattle of the door handle echoing through the damp, debt-littered hallway.

It wasn't even lunchtime, yet I'd been up since dawn *and* done a runner from a man in Neath, who was under the mistaken belief that we were marrying after my graduation. As I paused to consider my predicament, the recollection of a pile of mouldy chilli con carne dishes pricked my conscience: the remnants of that last Christmas meal we'd left behind, along with the overflowing bins and the menace of mice. I wasn't the only culprit. But where was everyone else?

It wasn't the first time the landlord had threatened us with eviction due to phantom rent payments, unwashed dishes and rancid student fridges. Frustrated, I lashed out, piercing the rotten wooden panel at the bottom of the door with my foot.

The upstairs window to my room opened with a jangle. A long red ribbon with a bell hung from the handle and batted in the breeze. On the sill, there was a new addition: a canary in a golden cage buffeting in the breeze. The collection of Norse Sagas I used for blocking out the draught was nowhere in sight.

A Chinese man leant out and stared down through thick-rimmed glasses. His denim jacket was buttoned up tight over his Adam's apple: an Asiatic Shakin' Stevens. Business Studies department no doubt; Economics at a push.

I was more upset about the canary than my eviction. I knew from my early budgie-keeping years that draughts could kill birds. I may not have washed my chilli dishes, but I *was* CND and Save the Whale. An occasional vegetarian too. There'd been a police arrest to prove my convictions, following an incident with three lesbian housemates, guided by the Runes and the fervour of protest. That was the night I'd learnt that truly 'biodegradable when it rains paint' *doesn't* need wire brushes, bleach and ten years of acid rain to remove it. The police had caught us, brushes in hand, painting 'shadows' in memory of the Hiroshima bombing. My portrait of a Scottie dog in the park, a reminder of the animals that perished, scoring ten out of ten with the local junior school. Animals were my thing. There'd be no cruelty to canaries in my room.

'Open the door, will you!'

The wind sucked the words from my mouth and hurled them out to sea.

'Landlord throw your stuff out,' the man said. 'This is my room now.'

'He can't do that!' I kicked the door again. 'I've got rights! Where's Nuclear Neil?'

'Big Man gone.'

I took a minute to digest this information. 'Gone where?'

'Tutor say Big Man play with Last Nerve. College dismiss him. Mother take him far away. Good thing. You go now. Bye.'

The bird flapped, the bell jangled, and the window banged shut.

My boxes were round the back by the bins, the unopened warning letters from my landlord still inside. The course books had gone, filched by some bastard and sold off at the student bookshop no doubt. My spider plant had survived and was sitting on the top, watered by Welsh rain. There was a pile of letters from Barclays Bank stuffed down the side. The paper had turned to mulch but there was no denying the red reminder ink which had leeched into the pulp. I didn't need to withdraw the envelope's sopping contents to know I was overdrawn. My student loan would have arrived by now, but it would only fill a hole and leave me back at zero. Dad was meant to send a 'top-up'. Maggie Thatcher had calculated that he could afford it, but 'topping up' implied you'd something in the kitty to start with. Dad had a mortgage on our family bungalow and was moonlighting all the hours god sent; flitting over to Dublin in the dead of night to repair planes when he should have been resting on his compulsory four days off. There was never enough money in the pot, and we were still trying to get back on our feet from the Laker Airways fiasco when the company he worked for had gone bust, and we'd nearly lost it all.

My mother was against university from the start. 'She'll only get married and have kids. We need to save up for her brother.'

But despite her yelling Dad was adamant. With an

AAB at A level – he reckoned I deserved my chance at further education. But now he was struggling to pay.

I was about to kick the door again, when I heard the basement window of the house next door squeak open.

'Oy! Over here!'

I crunched across the pathway to an identical Victorian semi, also converted into a student let. Below ground level there was a small window far from the reach of sunlight. I peered into the dark, fusty room below.

It was Vlad, my Russian neighbour. He was photosensitive and only emerged after sunset, living below ground level like the characters in *Hobson's Choice*. Vlad had developed a knack for recognising people by their shoes and he'd seen mine stomping up and down the pathway.

The rain was lashing down and my hair was plastered to my head. I'd abandoned my suitcase on the crazy-paving. 'Come on then!' I pleaded, 'Let me in!' It was Norman Bates creepy in Vlad's pit, but anything was better than this. The head bowed in assent and a hand reached up to close the window. I retrieved my Robin Reliant case, its fourth wheel lost at Neath bus station that morning and dragged it across the wet gravel. Vlad looked over my shoulder as if I might have been shadowed, pulled me inside and banged the door.

He was the oldest student I knew. With the delay his department has accorded him for deadlines (lack of mobility during sunlight hours mainly), he was in the fourteenth year of his PhD with no signs of completion.

He led the way through the stygian basement.

It was dark and a drip of cold, mildewy water ran down

my neck. It was the perfect place to grow mushrooms.

Bulky as a troglodyte, Vlad's inbuilt hunch was born from years of keeping his head down. His fine, blonde hair boasted that finger-in-a-socket style. His face was pimpled dough. But it was the room that did it. It carried that inimitable dank smell; that 'I left my clothes in the washing machine for three days before drying them' emanation, which permeated his cell; the same smell which, when I was in the library at night, led me straight to his cubicle.

We entered the cramped space he called home. My eyes scanned the shelves, clocking the familiar neatly stacked back-issues of *Playboy*. It was crunchy underfoot, the floor littered with the disembowelled computers which Vlad spent his time dismantling when not perusing porn.

'Tea?'

'Go on then.'

I prayed that just this once my friend might produce a silver caddy and fill it with strong black Russian leaves. Predictably, he fished a dried bag of Lipton's from the sink which, judging from its squeezed-around-the-waistline look, had already been used more than once.

With a quick flick of a match he lit the gas on a small camping-stove. The flame was the brightest thing in the room and cheerful as Christmas on a foggy night.

Vlad's rent was cheap because he was missing a proper window. His room was no more than a glory hole, lit by a feeble bulb which flickered on and off when the other tenants used the loo.

He picked up a torch and strapped it to his head, flicking

it on to interrogate me.

'Your lot have gone,' he said with satisfaction. Jealous of my other friends, I know he despised Nuclear Neil and the rugby crowd.

'I heard.'

'They dragged the tall one kicking and screaming. Two long groove marks on the shingles.'

'DHSS leaving you alone?' I asked, wanting to think about something else.

Vlad had acquired British citizenship and dole money, despite his PhD student status.

'Not so very bad. They sent me to work a couple of weeks in a darkroom at Boots.'

'Anything else been going on?'

'Da. Your fiancé Steve phoned the landline. He asked me to report when you arrived at the house.'

Half an hour later and I was back out in the stinging wind and rain, heading for the Student Welfare office. Vlad had told me what to say. He knew how to play the system. I hated asking for State help and was allergic to filling in forms. But there was no choice.

I needed to hurry. The weather was taking a turn for the worse. It wasn't unusual for the sea to hurl rocks against the line of shabby pink and blue guest houses on the seafront, smashing windows and unhinging signposts to old favourites like The Sea Bank Hotel, or the 'Sperm Bank' as the students called it. There was no-one out on the promenade. A few sad Christmas decorations blew in the wind.

I noticed an old woman dragging her shopping trolley along the seafront and hoped she wasn't Future Me. I didn't want to get stuck in Aberystwyth like Vlad; he'd be drawing his pension soon.

I was coming to the end of an era and sensed the cogs of the university churning as it spat out another batch. The future was uncertain, but I refused to turn into one of those students who clung on to their college because they were too afraid of the real world, post-uni.

Waves chewed at the wooden pier. I relished a quick blast of warmth as I passed the gaping mouth of the arcade with its garish row of bleating fruit machines. A lone student slumped on a stool, feeding coins into a flashing orifice, a can of lager in his other hand.

It was hardly Brideshead.

As I overtook the old lady she scowled. The locals weren't keen on students at the best of times (particularly once their grant was spent) and my outfit didn't help. I was wearing black fishnet tights, high-heel black evening shoes, a short skirt, and a long green jumper whose bobbles spoke of a long and rocky road since it first hung on a rail at Dorothy Perkins.

My coat was somewhere in South Wales with my soon-to-be-ex-fiancé who might already have burnt it. It was pretty crap coming back to find myself homeless, but at least I was on familiar ground. I just needed to survive the coming months.

CHAPTER 2

Christmas at Steve's house had been a sorry affair, involving, in no particular order: flu, the death of our two pet cockatiels Ralph and Elgan, the announcement of our wedding date, and the certitude that I needed to get as far away from Neath as possible.

I'd started going out with Steve at the end of my first year. Older than me, he'd graduated the previous summer, moving back home to take up a job in IT. Computer Science was the 'in' thing back in those days.

The Yuletide season was an endless round of arguments with no time to work, the result of which was a half-finished essay on Keats which lay in tatters in my bag. I choked back a rising sense of hysteria at how far behind I was, and how I'd fucked up my degree. Choppy waves slapped at the pier urging me to throw myself in and put both me and my tutor out of our misery for good.

Whenever I'd tried to take out my books, Steve's mum had conspired to drag me to Argos. The Priddy family behaved as if my degree was only a formality before my real life as a married woman began. Returning from the loo, I'd find my anthology of the Romantics' poetry replaced by a copy of the Littlewoods catalogue. The family was impervious to the need for essay writing. Steve's mum spent all day choosing electrical goods to put on our wedding list, whereas Steve spent his evenings out with his dad, down the pub or at the rugby.

When Steve's dad came home tipsy, after one pint too many, he made a show of saying how pleased he was that his son was marrying me, slipping his hand down the back of my dress as he did so. I told Steve, but he didn't believe me.

'Don't be daft,' he said. 'Any Welshman worth his salt would go for the front of the dress, not the back.'

One night at the Duke of Wellington, as we sat watching Cardiff vs. Neath on the giant screen, I headed the last of my snakebite and knew with sudden clarity, *I was living the wrong life.*

My friend Scarlett said it was the downfall of all English Literature students. We were trained to expect *more*. We wanted love, drama and passion. The works of literary fiction we studied ruined us for life. Whereas other students wrote theses on canned food or nuclear science, or went off and got well-paid jobs in IT, we wove ourselves into the plots of Gothic drama. At the very least we expected Mr Darcy or Heathcliff.

We didn't want toasters from Argos.

A married life with Steve would be the end, not the beginning; the final credits on a reel of film. I couldn't allow my life to be boxed and labelled so soon.

There had to be more.

Admittedly I had accepted the solitary diamond engagement ring paid for with Steve's beer and fruit machine allowance. At the time, it had seemed the perfect opportunity to experiment with saying 'yes' and having that symbolic band of trust slipped over my finger.

My parents' marriage was not a happy one for either of them. I'd spent my early years hiding under the dining-room table, pulling the tablecloth down and pretending to be safe inside my own home; trying to ignore the twist of my gut at the sound of screams as my mother threatened to throw boiling chip fat over my dad's head.

Part of me wanted a home and a family; a place in which to be secure – a grown-up version of the underside of that mahogany table – but another part yearned for adventure, pulling me away from anything conventional. It was a difficult combination of need and desire.

I'd accepted Steve's proposal because at the moment of his asking I'd felt loved and needed. Safe. But I hadn't processed the fact that marriage was final, thus precluding the possibility of anything else. Any *other* adventures. Not just romantic adventures, but adventures in life. My initial feelings of contentment and excitement were quickly replaced with glimpses of a humdrum future containing one main ingredient: *rugby*. Though not yet married we had already slipped into a monotonous routine. The stuff of nightmares.

My mother gloated.

It wasn't a trial run or a dress rehearsal for some future point in time. Half of South Wales was ordering hats and buying toasters.

The idea of saying anything other than 'yes' felt cruel and ungrateful; the long and heavy-hearted trail back to the pawnshop, where Steve had bought the ring, *awkward*. Cringe-worthy even. I had been brought up to make as little fuss as possible, and I knew Steve would react badly. He'd think there was *another bloke* and there'd be a scene.

All I had said was 'yes'.

Once I'd said this single word, events sped up like a video on fast-forward, gaining a momentum of their own. This was it. There was a wedding to plan and Steve's father didn't look like the sort of man who would understand, now the marquee had been booked, that this was a conceptual rehearsal for some future point in time. For some other man.

Cheques were flying out, and talks were of a wedding venue and even a new house near Steve's Mam and Dad. There was no question of my parents paying. Dad was keeping his head down doing refits of Turkish planes. There had been a recent discovery of yet another affair with an air hostess (married this time), and an incident in which my mother had pierced the plywood door in the kitchen by running at his heart with a carving knife. Dad had saved his life by slamming the door closed just in time. Since then he had broken up with his lady friend, handed the keys back to the love nest he had planned to rent, and purchased a new wedding ring for my mother; the first now lying on a rubbish dump at the bottom of a crushed can of Guinness. These events had drained not just the reserves of family patience, but savings too.

That night at the pub, shredding beer mats engorged with spilt lager and listening to the roar of spectators on the giant screen, I realised with overwhelming sadness that I could neither start my life, nor end it, with Steve.

As the crowds around me chanted, I wanted to punch the screen.

The whole wedding idea was superficial, naive, selfish and stupid. It had been an excuse to go down the pier for a party, to buy a new dress. And now my penance was a life of spectatorship stretching before me, season after season. It wasn't as if I even liked sport. Netball or iceskating were alright, of course, but that was only because of the glittering costumes and that sexy Torvill and Dean dance routine which had won the Olympics. There was nothing sexy about freezing by the side of a rugby field.

The whole family was obsessed.

'Why do they keep chanting?' I asked. 'What's the point of all this *NEATH, NEATH, NEATH*?'

'It's to show the boys are *together*,' Steve said.

Even Mrs Priddy chanted, her voice deliberately deep and sonorous.

There'd been bust-ups about my lack of sporting enthusiasm before. Not least that day when I'd sat with my back to the pitch, facing inwards towards the crowd, to shelter from the wind.

'*Unforgiveable,*' Steve had said, '*absolutely unforgivable. Some people would kill for a ticket and you sit with your back to the men in black.*'

'I was cold,' I replied, 'and bored.'

Steve's angry glower told me this was not the right answer.

The season never ended. Of course, the rugby season did finally wind to a close, but only to be replaced by something else: the cricket, the tennis, or the snooker. The whole year revolved around an endless season of sporting events, each bleeding into the next.

The only moment of sporting pleasure I'd known was the day I witnessed Imran Khan bat in his crisp white cricket jumper. But with little understanding as to how the game worked, even this vision of beauty merged into a dreamy fantasy, in which I wore a red veil, and sipped tea on a cool terrace while chatting to Imran, in the full knowledge that somehow Steve would disappear, and Imran would take me into his arms and make passionate love to me on a bed of silk, beneath a large rotating fan.

Reaching the end of the pier and dragging my case up the kerb in fury, I realised I didn't *want* to live in Neath, nor anywhere near Steve's parents. This is what *they* had assumed. I didn't want to populate any more crowded arenas with my offspring. I wanted to finish my English Degree and work at the Royal Shakespeare Company. I wanted to go home to England! After three years in Wales I was ready for Oxford, Cambridge or Stratford-upon-Avon. Somewhere *mellow*. Somewhere where the skies didn't spit hailstones in August and where people didn't sleep in rugby shirts or wear tops with a number on the back.

It wasn't that I wanted such an exciting life as my best friend Scarlett. I didn't want to sail down the Nile or make love in Pondicherry. Only recently she'd told me she had a job as an English teacher lined up in Milan, once we'd graduated, with plans for Bali the following year.

When I was ten years old my dad accepted a job for Malaysian Airline Systems and moved our family out to Petaling Jaya. At seven o'clock each morning I boarded a local bus to Kuala Lumpur leading my five-year-old brother on a treacherous journey. On one occasion this involved the bus rolling over a dead man who had fallen from a moped dangerously overladen with loaves of bread, the Bee Gees blaring out at full blast from our driver's radio as we felt the crush of bones against soft-sliced loaves. Such accidents were not uncommon incidents, earning the mobile bread deliverers the sobriquet 'jam sandwiches'.

We'd experienced adventure at an early age, including a failed kidnapping attempt when my mother, brother and I were held to ransom by a drugged-up taxi man who threatened to drive us to the jungle and string us from a tree unless we handed over all our money and jewels.

I was glad to return to England. My terrified ten-year old self breathing a sigh of relief as the plane touched back down at Manchester airport – Ringway, as my grandparents still called it back then. I didn't want to live in a country that ate monkey brains, having sobbed at the sight of those wooden tables out in the jungle with the circular holes cut through the tops for their heads.

On the other hand, I didn't want to live in a country that lived and breathed rugby either.

On that last morning with my fiancé, as dawn broke over the valleys of Neath, I woke early and crept from the room, calling a taxi before sunrise. Tiptoeing back to the bed one last time, I looked at Steve snoring in the cocoon of his favourite rugby shirt, knowing that this was the last time I would ever see him.

It was the end of our engagement.

If I stayed another day, I would have to face the music and break things off in person.

Or I could run away like a coward back to Aberystwyth.

The Student Welfare officer slammed the door of his metal filing cabinet. He opened a new file carefully avoiding my gaze.

He was a pale and shifty looking man.

'I'm sorry Miss Webb, but we are full. You moved out of halls two years ago and were deleted from our lists at this time. As you know, we give priority to first years and postgraduates.'

'I know, but my circumstances have changed. I have nowhere else to go.'

'Hmmm. I see.'

He glanced swiftly at my unkempt appearance as if comprehending this might be true.

'I'm worried I'll have to sleep in the Asda car park,' I said, trying to catch his eye.

There was a pause while the man shuffled papers with fingers speckled with ginger flakes the colour of warm Horlicks.

'Well, there is *one* room I suppose,' he said at last, cracking his finger joints.

'I only need one.' I forced a laugh.

'Highly unorthodox of course,' he continued, flicking through his folder. 'It's in the foreign students' block.'

In Aberystwyth at the time there was a strong sense of who was Welsh and non-Welsh. Who was British and who was foreign. Those so-called "overseas students".

'That's fine by me.'

He grimaced. 'Most are men of strict faith. All are mature students returning to study after what amounts, for some, as many years working in their own countries. In some cases, ruling their own countries. You do not tick any of my boxes.'

'I can see that. But I'll be ever so discreet. They won't know I'm there.'

There was a pause. It was nearly clocking-off time and the man's eyes edged to the clock on the wall.

'Very well. C-block Cwrt Mawr it is. Oh, and Miss

Webb, it's not so much how *you* will feel about *them*. It's how *they* will feel about *you*.'

CHAPTER 3

I mounted Penglais Hill, the mother of all university hills, my entire life stuffed into four black bin liners, care of Dyfed Council, bracing myself against wind and rain. Cwrt Mawr was a sprawling complex of concrete buildings. The units were linked by an artery of pathways and gardens. I saw through the windows that most had bare brick walls like prison cells. C-block was another world, heavy with the smell of garlic and garam masala. At the bottom of the corridor there was a busy looking kitchen where a group of men in long brown robes shouted at each other in an unfamiliar language. They were all older than me. There wasn't a woman in sight. The oldest looking man looked up and saw me at the door. The group stopped and stared as if I'd interrupted an important meeting at the United Nations. Embarrassed, I walked on.

I located C27 and closed the door behind me, pleased to find a spacious room with a small sink in the corner.

The walls were plastered, and being located on the ground floor, my room overlooked an open patch of grass. A group of students walked past clutching files. Perhaps I'd get some work done here at last. It was difficult to concentrate living in town, out of the shadow of the university, and it was a long time since I'd seen anyone carry a pile of books when a six-pack would do.

I unpacked my bag and changed out of my wet clothes.

Anxious for order in my life, I tipped the contents of my bags onto the bed. It wouldn't take long. Most things could go straight in the bin. There was a desk with a single shelf suspended above it, but I'd no more books with which to line it. The ones I hadn't already pawned had been stolen. Perhaps I could sell my engagement ring? I pushed the thought back. What was *wrong* with me? The relationship hadn't officially been pronounced dead and already I was selling the spoils. I knew it was desperation talking. It was going to be tricky if Dad couldn't send food money. As I changed into dry clothes, I pondered how to revise without any books. There was always the library of course, but it was a sure bet the books I needed would have been checked out for months by some 'on track for a double first' student.

Lost in thought, I took out my spider plant and unravelled its crocheted pot-holder.

I was on a chair, hanging it on a hook by the door, when there was a loud knock. The pot slipped from my hands and smashed to the ground. Cursing, I jumped down and opened the door to find a tall man, with jet-black hair and smooth olive skin, standing in the corridor. He was attractive, with distinctive features; the sort of romantic hero that would climb through the window and leave a box of chocolates by the bed in a 1970s advert. The man was wearing a black-and-white hound-tooth jacket, formal black trousers, a white frilly shirt and an oversized black bow tie.

'*Bonsoir, mademoiselle.* I beg pardon for interrupting.' He could easily have been an extra for '*Allo 'Allo.*

'I'm David and I have come to invite you for dinner. In France, we never allow a beautiful woman to dine alone. You will accept, I hope?'

Perhaps hunger had made me hallucinate.

He scrutinised me, head cocked, with immense eyebrows hovering expressively. He was intense and serious, his manner exquisitely unsettling.

It was laughable. My last two years had been spent on pub crawls with the Ifor Evans rugby team, listening to drunken men playing drinking games. Men for whom a romantic serenade would entail singing, 'Sit on my face and tell me that you love me' at my bedroom window before hurling the contents of their stomachs on their trainers.

I know that I had fallen into my relationship with Steve through desperation at not having had a proper boyfriend. A strict father – *Don't come crying to me if you're pregnant at sixteen!* – and seven years of single-sex education had seen to that. The man at my door was a character from a novel with a sexy French accent to boot. He was everything that had eluded me so far. I wanted to curtsy like Elizabeth Bennett, take his hand and float down the communal corridor.

As if reading my thoughts, David held out a hand, proffering a set of slender, sun-kissed fingers. A pause and then a beat. My heart pounded. Or was it my guilty conscience? One thing was undeniable: I was starving. There was a smell of garlic, cumin and coriander wafting up the corridor. It was an almost certain bet that my bank card would be swallowed if I inserted it in the cashpoint. I'd a roof over my head, but food was another matter.

'Go on then,' I said, avoiding the hand I so longed to take. 'Why not?'

I shook the plant from my shoe, crunched over shards of pot and rich Welsh soil, and followed David out of the door. I wasn't dressed for dinner. My hair lay damp on my shoulders, and my eyeliner had run halfway down my cheeks. As my friends knew, I never left the house without reapplying my pink blusher, but there was no time.

I was wearing my second favourite pair of black leggings now, and a long white jumper stretched out of shape with ghostly knee indentations where I'd pulled the hem down to keep warm.

In first year, back at Ifor Evans Hall of Residence, my hall-mate Cassie had bullied me out of my long Laura Ashley print dresses and forced me to buy a pair of leggings, some black pumps and several bold-coloured jumpers. Once I was fit to be seen on campus, we hung out in the Student Union bar, denim jackets slung over our shoulders, mine on loan from Cassie's collection. We'd lost touch in recent months; Steve had been more possessive than I should have allowed. Cassie was one of those girls who'd planned to make her first million by the time she was thirty and when I met her ten years later she was on track, with a fashionable apartment, a top job in insurance and a convertible sports car. Steve was wary of my single friends, and after one night too many with my minder glowering in the background, Cassie had dropped me.

Left in charge of my own wardrobe from then on, I'd morphed into the love child of an eighteenth-century milkmaid crossed with an eighties pop star. Stylistically ill-matched, but keenly aware of each other's physical presence, I followed this tall and gangly Frenchman down the hall corridor, David looking as if he was about to lead me onto the ballroom floor at Blackpool Tower.

In the kitchen, long canteen-style tables were grouped together in the middle of the room. A row of students, mostly male, were seated down both sides. All were older than me, mature for the most part, in their thirties if not forties. David was the youngest, in his mid-twenties.

There was Ahmad from Bagdad, Rafi who lived in Benazir Bhutto's palace in Pakistan, and Taloob who was a Pakistani prince placed firmly under Rafi's heavy wing. I was introduced to Josephar from Botswana who studied Agriculture, and a youngish guy, with a pock-marked face and tight jeans called Ramid, who was busily licking the neck of an attractive Malaysian girl called Michelle. He raised a phlegmatic eyebrow to say hello. Most of the students were on the MBA course. They were all studying 'useful' things: Business, Farming, Politics, Computers, Soil. I felt I was wasting Government money. How many jobs required Middle English or Old Icelandic?

David told me it was Rafi's turn to cook dinner. He was stirring the contents of an enormous pot with a wooden spoon. He was stout, with a compact barrel of a stomach which swelled his long brown robes. He alternated between smoking and sipping from a tumbler of whisky. This surprised me. I was used to the Welsh not drinking on a Sunday – not officially at least, though there was lots of shuffling at the off-licence with brown paper bags, because of the prohibition on the Sabbath in Dyfed. But I was surprised to see a muslim man drinking.

Later I would learn that, for these students, Aberystwyth was a moment out of time; a wormhole in space into which they had crawled so that an Iraqi might dine with a Palestinian or an Israelite, and share tobacco and good food; it was a place where they were forced to fend for themselves, cook and do laundry for the first time, though back home most had servants and wives – several wives in some cases.

The strip lights flickered, and as the mist from the sea came in and night set, the first-floor kitchen hovered like a golden ball in the night above campus. My fellow travellers had come from far. Some had fought in wars. I'd not yet lived. My wars had been at home indoors with an OCD mother, or at a single-sex comprehensive school, where I could count the number of times I'd been allowed to bring friends home on one finger. Was that the reason I'd slipped so quickly into a claustrophobic relationship with Steve?

A grey-haired man from Glasgow called Iain joined us. He was the only other European. Small and wiry with a handle-bar moustache, he'd been in battle too. In a previous life, he was an army captain, but had dropped out with 'a bout of pacifism'. He helped himself to a glass of Rafi's whisky, rolled himself a cigarette and started ribbing with Josephar, the two men playing fisty-cuffs. Iain wore check carpet-slippers, neatly pressed jeans and a navy-blue pullover, the kind fishermen wear. He jiggled his knee nervously as he talked, swinging the slipper on the end of his foot, rolling the next cigarette before he'd finished the first. The table between us was laden with cardboard boxes full of wine and beer and lots of supermarket brand cola.

David hugged Ahmad from Bagdad. 'My brother', he said, 'has been in the war and in the desert many years. Now we enjoy friendship and good food.'

Ahmad smiled. He didn't speak much English. His eyes were red and bleary, his hair a halo of grey frizz. He wouldn't look at me to begin with, and despite his rough appearance I realised he was gentle as a spring rabbit with a voice soft as dew. 'Yes, my brother,' he said to David, 'my *Jewish* brother.' He laughed. 'Who could imagine?'

Ahmad's face was scarred and pitted. David told me that his friend was also in his mid-twenties, and when he saw my look of disbelief Ahmad took out a crumpled photograph. It was hard to see the resemblance between the slim, smoothskinned man in the photo, taken just a few years earlier, and the man standing before me. David talked angrily about chemicals, Iran and the desert. I should have known more about the war this man had fought in. I should at least have known how to pinpoint his country on the map.

'He may be deported if there's another war,' David said. 'He's worried about his Masters. But tonight, we eat Rafi's dal and Pervaiz's chicken curry.'

Pervaiz sat in the corner with Taloob. He smiled a lot but didn't say much. A lithe man, bald, with a shiny crown and thick, black glasses.

'Ah, Pervaiz,' said David, 'respect to this man, for he is not such a lowly student as us. Pervaiz is a great lecturer in business, overseeing my investigations into the canned food industry, and keeping his sharp eye not just on his friends from Pakistan, but on all of C-block.'

Pervaiz nodded and smiled again.

'I am both tutor and chaperone,' he said, pointing to his friend. 'This is Taloob. He is a prince from my country, so I must keep an eye on him if I do not wish to be shot,' he winked, 'for Taloob is not always good and reasonable. He gives me all these worry lines.' He crumpled his brow to demonstrate.

'Why, what does he do?' I asked.

Taloob answered for his chaperone. 'I have dared to fall in love with an Italian woman named Ombretta, whom I wish to be my bride. But this is not something of which my family, or Rafi, approve.'

Taloob smiled and shook his attractive head. He was dressed in simple but expensive-looking designer clothes, wearing jeans and a white linen shirt. There was something of the young Imran Khan about him. He needed only a cricket jumper. I could see why Ombretta had fallen for him.

Rafi sweated over the pan, beads trickling down his face into his twirling moustache.

The wind drove the rain against the window, rattling the panes, a gentle reminder we were still in Wales. Across the campus on the other side of the gardens were kitchens identical to this one, with students bent over electric hotplates, illuminated like figures on a giant screen long before reality TV. Two students arrived with a large cardboard box piled high with vegetables. They talked to one another in Chinese, filling the fridge, then hastily retreated to their rooms. 'They are the only people who do not wish to eat with us,' said David. 'We have extended the arm of friendship many times but they are happiest alone. We do not judge. Here in C-block everyone must be good to each other and if they are happy, this makes us happy too.'

The plates on the table were chipped and ill-assorted. I was placed next to David, who brandished screw-top wine as if it was a *grand cru*, and given the job of lighting candles stuck in old wine bottles.

I was grateful no-one had asked me to cook. My mother made our kitchen a no-go zone when we were children. My brother and I were forbidden to enter her sacred space; summoned to the dining room for meals and banned from opening the fridge to serve ourselves. The result of this was that I arrived at university not knowing how to switch on an oven or boil an egg. Throughout my first year I ate in Penbryn Hall of Residence canteen. In our second year Cassie brought home an industrial-sized pack of frozen fish fingers, a massive bag of peas and a family-size pack of dried mashed potato. We lived for a term on this tasty but limited menu. Cassie, the only student to leave university with her bank account in credit, carefully distributing two fish fingers each, per meal. When Steve came along he replaced Cassie, regularly providing one of his two stock favourites: chilli con carne or spag bol. The rest of the time we ate pizza at the Student Union.

Tonight, in C-block, the formica table was laden. Rafi piled my plate high. I put aside my vegetarian ideals and devoured the chicken, knowing I'd need some meat on my bones in the lean months ahead. It certainly beat staying in my room alone with a spider plant for company.

Habte from Ethiopia arrived late from the library and joined us, together with an excitable man with a squeaky voice called Jaime from Chihuahua. No-one waited to be invited; they took a plate from the cupboard and helped themselves from the bowls in the middle of the table. Shamilla from Malaysia, in blue batik dungarees, squeezed in at the end of the table. She shared a room with Michelle in an all-girls block opposite. Michelle disengaged Ramid's tongue so that she could eat.

'Every night it's like this,' David said. 'We never know who's coming so we cook for plenty. No-one goes hungry.' He was flushed now and had lost the jacket. His shirt had been carefully ironed and I imagined him dressing for dinner. It made a change from those 'straight out of the dryer' rugby shirts the rugby boys wore at the Union. David clearly didn't believe that clothes used for sporting activities could double up as dinner wear. He was attentive to me and when he laid his hand across mine to ask if I would care for *a little more Bordeaux,* there was an inner jolt of pleasure sadly lacking whenever Steve fizzed open a can of Strong Brew.

When we had finished our instant coffee and the men had smoked their pipes and roll-ups, David stood abruptly.

'Come,' he said. 'We'll get your coat from my room.'

My coat was in Neath, but I followed my host down the long corridor.

Up and down C-block, the fire doors were slamming as students returned to their rooms for the night. They were off to study, not heading out for *a night on the tap* like the Ifor Evans boys. I thought of Steve back home in South Wales. I wondered if it was darts tonight, or if he was staying in with his mam and dad. I thought of the wedding list and of all his aunties who had contributed. Some of them were pensioners. It wasn't moral to take their money even if Auntie Jean had won the sandwich toaster at Bingo.

My current financial situation could only be due to bad karma.

The solitaire diamond in my ring dug into my palm like a secret.

I didn't want to be branded, however sparklingly. Or to *belong* to someone else.

That's what marriage is all about, you dozy mare, my inner father cried.

We sat on the bed. David pressed a button on a cassette player. Richard Clayderman playing *Frantic Piano*. He smelt strongly of aftershave. The moment should have been ridiculous, a cliché to run from, but I was rooted to the spot.

The course of my life was about to change. The *thing* I called 'desire', as it coursed through my every fibre, was the jolt of a new pathway as it carved out a future I had not planned. We stumble into such determining moments; life is a series of them. Their prelude may be nothing more than a plate of tarka dal and a fictitious coat. There were no flashing lights to warn us.

Invisible stagehands came in as we sat on the narrow student bed beneath David's giant Betty Blue poster. They carried out the painted scenery of Cheshire and Wales, replacing it with views of Paris and the French countryside with its vineyards and Chateaux; the backdrop against which my adult life would now play.

'May I kiss you?' David asked with refreshing simplicity. I noticed he didn't have to get drunk to say this, and he didn't make a clumsy lunge towards me. The question was asked simply.

'I can't,' I said, pressing my ring deeper into my palm, 'I'm engaged.'

'That is a grave pity, for one so young.'

Graves made me think of early death and lost opportunity. I couldn't waste this moment. It was the most intense I'd ever known.

'It's awful,' I said, 'but I'm *not* getting married. I don't want to anymore. But Steve, my fiancé, doesn't know that yet. You must think I'm horrible, telling *you* first.'

'*Mais non*,' he said, placing his hand on mine, 'but now that I *do* know, there is perhaps, how shall I say, *a little compromise* possible?'

He took both my hands and pressed them together beneath his own. I was shaking. I wanted to kiss him. I didn't want to go home. But it was *wrong*. As I closed my eyes I saw a line of toasters and waffle-makers spread out on a table like prizes to be won at a quiz show. Steve's mum and dad were clapping as some cheesy compere shouted at me to 'Come on down'. Only I was round the back of Television Centre with a long-legged Frenchman.

I grabbed the white starched university sheet from the bed and pulled it over my head, draping it around me.

'Maybe through the sheet,' I said. 'Maybe that wouldn't count.'

He smiled and pushed me back onto the pillow. 'Through the sheet is not counting at all,' he said. 'See how our lips do not touch.'

And so I kissed my first Frenchman, and though it

was only through a university sheet, I knew deep down there were tricky times ahead.

CHAPTER 4

It was a full six months later when Rafi and my other friends stood on the station platform to say goodbye. David was already in Paris. Taloob, my Imran Khan lookalike friend from Pakistan, was the only one too upset to attend. I found a note from him pushed under my door early that morning. 'I hope life is always kind to you,' it said.

I hoped so too.

The night before, back in Cwrt Mawr kitchen, in a last-ditch attempt to salvage something from his new European life, Taloob had asked me to marry him, telling me it was finished with the Italian and he would take me to Pakistan, where he would treat me like a princess. He too saw the window of opportunity closing as his time at university ended. The proposal ended in a dismal, tear-drenched kiss from Taloob infused with our mutual grief: Taloob at the idea of returning to a strict life in Pakistan; me with the anguish of an uncertain welcome in Paris from my estranged boyfriend.

Both of us were lost and clinging to a dream, but I wondered as I boarded the train if the idea of running away to a palace in Pakistan was any more ridiculous than the fool's errand on which I was about to embark.

That evening, Ahmad tried to joke Taloob out of his tears by telling him I was worth no more than half a camel's leg now, being Spoilt Goods and all. We laughed, but deep down I knew Ahmad meant it. I'd slept with two men: one a Welsh Methodist; the other a French Orthodox Jew. Oh, and there had been that *slight* fling with a Greek Cypriot who looked like Tony Curtis in *Some Like It Hot*. That was far too many lovers by Muslim standards, and it had cost me any number of camel legs.

My train pulled into the station and a few stray travellers climbed on board. I was making the long journey to Stansted where I had a flight booked, to take me to Beauvais airport on the outskirts of Paris where I would begin my new life.

Rafi, the eldest of the group, placed a podgy hand on my shoulder. Two hard brown eyes stared intently into my own.

'You know I think you are a fool,' he said. 'No good will come of this wild goose chase. If you were my daughter I would take you home and make you clean goat pens until you saw sense.' He winked but nodded a little sadly, so I knew the message was serious.

My father had said pretty much the same thing as this polite Pakistani gentleman. *You need your flaming head testing,* were his exact words.

44

I hung my head miserably. Rafi had not finished.

'You know that David has told you to let him go. You know you follow him in vain, despite his wishes and contrary to our advice. But we, your friends from Cwrt Mawr C-block, wish you well, and we will be here for you, should you wish to return.'

Rafi closed his arms around me, and then let me go, casting a glance to the skies, as if there was no hope for this foolish girl who had wasted enough of his time. My surrogate family hugged me hard. There was nothing more to be said. I pushed myself out of the group and ran to the train before I could change my mind. I was just in time as the guard blew his whistle and the train pulled out of the station. I settled back on the start of my long, seven-hour journey. There would be time to think as we cut through oppressive purple mountains and dank green valleys. Turning from my fellow passengers I pressed a damp cheek against the cold window pane, bidding a silent farewell to the sheep who clung to the hillside in mist and fog.

In my pocket, there was a plastic bag filled with sticky globular gulab jalum cakes. I took one out, bit into the soft syrupy interior and tasted rose water through the salt of my tears. I watched the rain pelt the dirty grey windows and played back the last few months, events racing through my mind as fast as the telegraph poles outside the train window, punctuating my mind with incidents which were both joyous and painful to remember. David being Jewish had meant nothing to me. Not at first. I had no idea that being non-Jewish would make me unworthy. On the night I began to take it seriously we were walking home from the Student Union bar, arm in arm. David was wearing his long, dark wool overcoat, which, with his thick black hair and brows always gave him that sombre 'Death is at the door' look.

He wasn't happy.

I'd just feasted on a Friday-night Union pizza with prawns on the top, despite David's protests. Angry now he told that me since Unclean Foods had traversed my tongue, he couldn't kiss me.

I laughed.

'What do you mean, you *can't* kiss me?'

'Prawns, they are not kosher. They do not have – how do you say? – the little wings, to swim with.'

'Fins.'

'*Oui, exactement.* They do not have fins or *écailles.* How is it? Scales I think. Yes, scales. And they have been in your mouth, so I can't kiss you.'

When I laughed, he strode off so fast I couldn't catch him. I ran behind to pull him back. I wanted to prove that his desire to kiss me was greater than these antiquated rules which felt a bit OCD to me.

I'd had enough of rules with no rhyme or reason from my mother. *Don't touch black bin liners. Don't go near sewer pipes. Cross the road if you see a tramp.*

It seemed unjust that although it was okay for David to kiss *me* when I was still *engaged* (the toaster and sandwich makers had all gone back to Argos now, and I'd been told in no uncertain terms by Steve's mum 'never to darken their doorway again') *he* wouldn't kiss *me* because of five shrivelled up prawns topped with cheese and garlic, currently rebirthing in a sea of warm lager.

David pushed me back, hard enough to mean business, holding me at arm's length.

'*Non,*' he said, '*Stop!*'

'Don't be *ridiculous,*' I retaliated. 'How can you believe such *bollocks*? What do you want me to eat? Locusts?'

He gave me *that* look, all dark and brooding, then stormed off to Cwrt Mawr.

I ran after him. For a few minutes, the only sound was our feet on gravel and heavy breathing.

As we reached the lighted doorway, he spun around waving his long arms in the air.

'*This is the whole problem!*' he cried. 'This is what you refuse to understand. I am Jewish, and you are not. *Je suis Juif.* It changes everything.'

'Well, if it means that much to you, *I'll* be Jewish,' I said. 'I'll be *juif*. Or should that be *juive*?'

It was better than being a rugby widow.

'You think it's that easy, do you?' he said. 'You think you can just be Jewish. like that?' He clicked his fingers.

'I don't see why not,' I said, certain it was all about learning some scripture or something; a religious ceremony perhaps. Special clothes?

In A level RE the Jews never came off very well. They had killed Christ for a start. Surely the fact I loved David enough to *want* to be Jewish counted for something? Not everyone would go to such lengths for love. It showed how respectful I was of all this crap and how seriously I took his religion.

'They will never accept you,' he shouted. 'Neither my family nor my community. You will always be an outsider.'

'But that's –' I tried to conjure up the worst word I could find, hit him where it hurt, '– that's *racist*. That's just as bad as the Nazis in the war.'

This last comment propelled him up the final and steepest part of the hill, so I was gasping for breath by the time I caught up.

He reached the top and turned like a fury.

'Yes, you mention the *Nazis*, and I'm telling you, because of what they did, because of what happened, it is important that our race, our people, do not mix. We must protect ourselves. We have lost too much. And I must find a Jewish woman and a Jewish wife to be the mother of my children.'

'And that's more important than loving me?' I asked. David breathed in deeply and grabbed my shoulders. 'Yes,' he said, weary now. 'You will not understand me, and maybe you will even hate me. I should have stopped this before it even started. I am a big shellfish (he meant 'selfish') following my passions and desires and not my head. But yes, it is more important than you.'

I'd finished the last of the galub jalums and started on a packet of Jelly Babies. I felt a bit sick. I bit red and green heads off and pulled fat little bodies into long stretched pieces of jelly, until they turned white.

After that first night of passionate love-making on a single bed, our bodies buffed by scratchy college blankets, there had been an inevitable build-up to David's departure back to France. David had fallen in love too, or so he said. But his faith had determined to contain our love in the framework of those last few months at university.

He scored the date of his departure onto a Credit Agricole bank calendar on the back of his door, next to the fire escape instructions; the only thing to hang there other than his *Betty Blue* poster.

At first, the date sat securely in the future, long after the presentation of his thesis on canned foods and at the start of the summer and my *own* Finals. There was plenty of time to enjoy each other. And still plenty of time to change his mind.

'When I leave, we must never see each other again,' he'd say, 'or only as friends. And even then, not for some time, not until our feelings have died.'

You'll see, I thought. When that day comes, you won't be strong enough to end this for real, because I *know* how happy you are with me.

But as the months went by, *février, mars, avril, mai...* I realised that David had, if anything, grown more resolute. As he grew used to me and the novelty of our passion wore off, I suspected that he looked at other women with new interest. Michelle perhaps? Hadn't there already been some mild flirtation in the air, before Ramid wedged his appendages between them? Rafi had told me as much in warning; David is a man away from his country and the restrictions of his family. He is drawn to women like a hawkmoth to a flame; driven by a part of his body which is housed neither in his brain nor in his faith – a dangerous combination for as foolish a heart as yours.

I grew bitter. If David had been so keen on his faith all along, why didn't he behave at university as an Orthodox Jew should? Why wasn't he cowering from light-switches on a Friday as my phobic mother cowered from bin men on a Monday? How dare he seduce me knowing the sell by date on our love was stamped as clearly as on a tin of canned food.

Maybe now he'd 'had' me (in the Old Testament sense), he wanted more women from around the world to chalk up on his headboard. Who else would he dangle beneath his *Betty Blue* poster? Michelle from Malaysia, or Fung from China? And what about that Japanese girl who never spoke to anyone, but who'd worn her national costume at the last ball in his honour? He'd had his photo taken with her. Maybe he wanted to sleep with her too?

Perhaps this whole MBA course, the one which I spent most of my time editing, was an interlude in which to seduce all the non-Jewish girls he could find, before settling for someone *worthy* enough to bear his children.

Whatever the religious reasons David gave, my insecure heart could only surmise that the real reason was *me*.

I wasn't good enough.

It would be a familiar pattern; seeking love in places where it couldn't be found; pushing and pushing until the final rejection came to confirm my worst fear – I was undeserving of love. When love was too possessive, or too controlling, as Steve's had been, I pulled away, preferring to struggle for affection than to have it bestowed in profusion. To feel worthy, I needed to conquer the heart of a man who didn't want me much to begin with. With the Sword of Damocles above my head, and chronically behind with my revision, it was easy to slip into depression in the weeks before my Finals.

During this dismal period I'd wandered up past the Sperm Bank Hotel to the top of Constitution Hill on more than one occasion, sodden with self-pity and as melodramatic as Catherine Earnshaw when Heathcliff had fled. For the hundredth time, I'd considered hurling myself into the sea to make a point. But death would deny me the only satisfaction that could possibly come from such an action: the satisfaction of watching David's face on the day he finally realised what his unreasonable actions had led me to do.

Then came David's surprise gift. A trip to Paris for my twenty-first birthday, and a long weekend of love-making in a shabby hotel near the Gare du Nord far from his parents' reach.

The quartier around the Gare du Nord wasn't much different from Cwrt Mawr; just as international and with a million mopeds to boot. We made love and wept, made love and wept, our love-making punctuated by long walks around the city, trailing miserably round Le Louvre, down the rue de Rivoli and up the Eiffel Tower.

On my flight home, I knew two things with absolute certainty: firstly, David wasn't going to change his mind; secondly, Spencer had taken over 500 pages to get to the point with *The Faerie Queene*. It would be easier to impress my lover and part the waves of the Red Sea, than it would be to regurgitate this particular ode in time for my exams.

There were poems. And then there was *The Faerie Queene*.

Not the same thing at all.

I scrunched up the empty bag of Jelly Babies as the train screeched to a halt in Shrewsbury. A cup of British Rail tea would have hit the spot, but I was broke. Again. The last of my overdraft facility spent on a mini-break in a seedy hotel in the north of Paris.

With his departure, David's letters arrived as frequently as always, bearing news of his Gallic life: long missives in curling handwriting, full of loving endearments, as if we were waiting to be reunited. Tender words scratched with the sharp nib of his pen into blue airmail paper: *My love, my little flea, my sweet dove, my girl with eyes of deepest blue.* Yet every letter ended with the same proviso: *Do not wait for me. Do not love me. Let us lay these passions to rest, so that in time I may become your one true friend.*

So why exactly was I going to Paris?

The main reason was to improve my language skills – or

so I convinced myself.

I might have left university with a bog-standard 2:2, and learnt the hard way that Spencer was not best skim-read when my heart was broken and my future dependent on wafer thin scraps of airmail paper, but at last, I told myself, something educational could be salvaged from this.

Love had revived my 'O' level French skills like a phoenix from the flames. Surely it would be a pity to let that wondrous linguistic bird flop right now? Speaking French was a useful skill, wasn't it? Convinced, I enrolled on a French course at l'Institut Catholique in the rue de Rennes.

This had nothing to do with David at all.

The challenge was to find a way to live in Paris and fund both my trip and my language lessons. Fate provided me with a curious answer to my conundrum.

A letter arrived from an old sixth-form friend, Jessica, who informed me in a familiar spidery hand that she was *off to live in Paris*. She would be working as a *jeune fille au pair* in the western suburbs, where she would have a room, basic salary, free board and lodgings. Not only this, she was going to study at the Institut Catholique, rue de Rennes.

It was such a strange coincidence, I convinced myself that The Universe had conspired to nudge me on my way across the Channel.

The real point of Jessica's journey, she later told me, was to track down Samuel Beckett, who it was said hung out on Friday nights at a small bar in Montmartre, where local groups played live music. This secret address, unknown to tourists, was somewhere down a side alley, off the beaten track. As an existentialist at heart, Jessica was determined to sit at the bar with her favourite author, as the old boys played the accordion, and get to the bottom of the great man himself over a glass of fine house brandy.

Pride forbade me from admitting I was tailing a man who'd dumped me.

I bought a copy of *The Lady* magazine that same morning, where the answer to my problems lay between its sweet-smelling glossy pages. The advert stood out from the more formal ones around it, having been composed by the children themselves.

We are 3 French children, aged 12, 9 and 6, seeking a jeune fille au pair to join our family in a big house close to Paris. Looking for an intelligent girl, who likes to smile. Would prefer if she could cook us tasty meals, play fun games and care for us while maman and papa are out of the house. English mother tongue preferred. Only Delphine speaks English. Please send photo as Clémence can't yet read. Apply to...
PS. We don't like mint sauce on our meat or baked beans.

A whole new adventure without David! Though who was to say if I found myself in his *quartier* I might not look him up?

David had taken pains to keep me away from his family home during our trip to Paris. Luckily, at the start of our relationship, he had written his address in my diary. Something I'm certain he would not have done by the end. He lived on la rue des Rosiers, which conjured images of rose bushes blooming around a forbidden doorway, a froth of fairy-pink buds at the windows, like Sleeping Beauty's palace. I would go there and chop them down, regardless of the thorns, and make him see that *love would win the day*. I would, I would, I would.

The train lulled me into a gentle sleep. I curled my legs around the bag that contained all my worldly possessions and tried to shut out Rafi's now distant voice: 'No good will come of this. No good will come of this'.

And louder still, that of my father's: 'You flaming idiot. You dozy bloody mare.'

CHAPTER 5

Paris, La Banlieue

I awoke in panic, in an unfamiliar room, and sat bolt upright. The walls were covered with hessian and punctured with multicoloured pins like an infant-school classroom. The shutters were closed, but sunlight crept through the slats. It must have been around nine. I wondered if I should be up and doing something useful, though of course the only thing I wanted to do was to find David.

The night before I had been met at Beauvais airport, north of Paris, by a tall and angular man, holding a piece of cardboard inscribed with the words 'Axel Blanchard'. He had written his own name on the card, not mine.

The man spoke good English and greeted me with a formal handshake. To reassure me, he presented me with a handwritten note from Madame Blanchard, his wife, in which she explained in perfect English that she had injured her leg playing tennis the day before and was laid up in bed. Her husband had come to take me home.

The journey home, in the smart family car, passed pleasantly enough, with polite conversation and only the occasional panic that this grey-suited man might be a dapper serial killer who had somehow done away with Madame Blanchard.

We skirted round Paris on the *Périphérique* at over 100 kilometres an hour. The roadside fell away into a blur of concrete and exhaust fumes. Monsieur Blanchard dodged the traffic with quick flicks of his slender wrist on the power steering. Although it was Sunday, he was dressed in office-style clothes: the cuffs of his shirt were white and starched beneath the steel-grey jacket, the hands of his Rolex inched rhythmically forwards.

Soon I would be the one starching the cuffs of this neat man. Madame Blanchard had made it clear on the phone that ironing was to be one of my principle duties.

If I'd stayed with Steve, I would have been washing mud out of rugby shirts in Neath. As it was, I would be pressing neat French shirts into place and looking after the clothes of this cool-mannered, grey-suited man, who wasn't to know that I had never ironed a work shirt in my life. Would I have to deal with his underwear? What sort of underpants did a man as frosty as Axel Blanchard wear?

I turned my face to the car window to hide a smile and caught a glimpse of the Eiffel Tower, illuminated with a thousand golden lights – snatched away before I could relish it, as the car plunged into the depths of a long, acrid-smelling tunnel.

Twenty minutes later and we were back into fresh air, pulling up in a quiet, tree-lined avenue. Monsieur Blanchard parked outside the large, wrought-iron gates of a stone house that looked early nineteenth century in style.

Later I would learn that this *maison bourgeoise* was typical of the type of house that dotted the leafy western suburbs of Paris, and sold for the equivalent of a life-sized reproduction of the Eiffel Tower. Gold plated. It was of course a privilege of the lucky few to own such a property, and to have a garden so close to Paris. Most families were squashed into apartment blocks, reliant on local parks for their greenery. But I knew none of this as I stepped from the car and looked up curiously at my new home.

Once inside Monsieur Blanchard indicated that my room was on the top floor on the right but did not accompany me up the stairs. He bade me a curt goodnight and disappeared through a set of double doors.

I climbed the polished wooden staircase, found my room and climbed straight into bed, falling into a deep sleep from which I did not stir until early light.

I swung out of bed and tiptoed across the squeaking parquet to open the shutters. The iron bars were stiff, and I pushed and pulled with difficulty until the metal bar gave, and I could peer out over a row of red rooftops.

I scanned the horizon for a glimpse of the Eiffel Tower. There was no sign of it. The Blanchard household was in the wealthy western suburbs of Paris and, as Mr Blanchard had explained during our car journey, was situated closer to Versailles than to Paris.

The only buildings I could see on the distant horizon were a cluster of tall skyscrapers, rising from what looked like mist or pollution, and beyond those, a white archway. I knew from my reading, that this was La Défense, where Monsieur Blanchard had his offices. The Grande Arche was aligned symmetrically with the Arc de Triomphe, thus creating a direct and symbolic passageway from the new business centre to the heart of the ancient city. I also knew that somewhere, through these imposing gateways, David was moving on with his life, oblivious to the fact that I was here.

I had yet to meet Madame Blanchard. The night before, her voice had rung through the darkened corridors of the household, as I crept up the stairs with my bags: '*Karen, bienvenue. A demain.*'

I knew, from the clipped explanations barked by Monsieur Blanchard before bedtime, that he would have taken the three children to school by now, but that from tomorrow morning onwards this would be my job. As things stood, I was surely alone in the house with Mrs Blanchard who was laid up in bed, in pain. Perhaps I should make her some tea or breakfast, but I didn't yet know my way around this shadowy house, nor what was expected of me.

What would Jane Eyre do?

I dressed, and explored my floor to find the children's bathroom and three rooms with neatly made beds next to my own. We were in a separate wing of the house from the grown-ups. The bathroom was painted in playschool red, with easy-to-wash, hospital-white floor tiles. There were three toothbrushes in the holders, large, medium and small, like the Three Bears. I unpacked my washbag and placed my tooth brush in the cup, showered quickly, combed my hair and put on some make-up. Not too much. I couldn't imagine any woman with a twisted ankle wanting her *jeune fille au pair* slinking down to breakfast looking like a glamour-puss. I wondered how elegant a French lady like Madame Blanchard was? The only French women I knew were the ones in perfume adverts and I was sure that my new employer must be exquisite. Her husband was not unattractive by any means, but so formal in his suit and tie that it was difficult to imagine him in any context other than a board meeting.

I tied my hair back in a serious knot, a respectable Miss Jane Eyre type who had come to lend a helping hand, and tiptoed down the grand, turning staircase. The wood was neatly polished and smelt of bee's wax, the walls of the middle floor covered in tasteful modern oils.

The gilded doorway through which Monsieur Blanchard had vanished the night before was firmly shut. I pressed my ear to the wood but there wasn't a sound, so I crept downstairs where I discovered a kitchen, a dining room, a music room and a rather grand salon which led onto a veranda. There was a large garden visible through the French windows (what word did the French use for 'French windows'?).

I decided it was best to wait in the kitchen; a suitably servile place to be.

A woman with a colourful green turban on her head walked in carrying a duster. She jumped and then smiled, saying something which I didn't understand. Seeing my look of confusion, she repeated her name – Fuschia, and gesticulated with her duster to show me what she was doing.

There was a baguette on the table with some butter and jam, as well as a tray, with an empty coffee cup, littered with crumbs. Fuschia pointed to the tray, miming an eating and drinking motion.

I sat down and buttered myself a piece of bread. Fuschia was busy scrubbing the coffee pot. I glanced around but couldn't see a kettle on the work surface. I timed Fuschia's next exit and quickly opened the cupboards, scanning the shelves for a box of tea. Not a box of PG Tips in sight. There was, however, a green box labelled 'Chinese gunpowder'. I unscrewed the lid and sniffed the leaves, which the manufacturer hadn't bothered to bag. There was still the problem of the missing kettle. Fuschia returned and appeared to understand my problem. She gabbled something and took out a big pan, filled it with water and put it on the hob. This seemed a complicated way to make a cup of tea, but over the next few months I would learn that tea wasn't such a ritual in France as it was in England, and most people resorted to boiling water in a pan on the hob or, even worse, pouring lukewarm water from the microwave onto a teabag, creating a frothy film on top of the tea.

I tipped water from the heavy-based pan into the cup, spilling it onto the recently scrubbed worktops. How annoying! This wouldn't have happened with a kettle, and now I had to use the neatly ironed teacloth to wipe it up. I was making a mess for Fuschia.

I ate, worrying about the deluge of crumbs falling from my baguette and thinking that I shouldn't be stuffing my face, but washing the children's clothes or tidying their rooms. The teacup was full of leaves and I thought back with longing to those neat bags we had in Cwrt Mawr kitchens. Maybe I'd put too many leaves in, as they appeared to have soaked up most of the water, but there was now no more of it left in the pan; plus, there was the question of where to put the leaves. They were sure to block the sink, and the kitchen bin gaped open, scrubbed within an inch of its life with bleach, and awaiting a new bin-liner.

I finished my first French breakfast with indigestion and rushed to the sink, eager to wash the plate and knife. I wiped the table-top and put everything back, stuffing the Chinese gunpowder leaves onto the top soil of a plant in the kitchen window.

Perhaps I should try and find Fuschia and see if she needed any help. I found her in the salon, at the back of the house, polishing wooden statues. The walls were lined with enormous oil paintings of an abstract nature. The largest of the collection was a swirling mass of cream, brown and black, which reminded me of the storms off the coast of Aberystwyth, producing my first pang of homesickness. The artist had scrawled his name at the bottom right of the picture: HUGO. There was something badtempered about the painting – a lugubrious fellow no doubt.

Beneath the painting was a wooden sculpture as high as my hips. I ran my hand over it. The head was smooth and rounded with a crack running across the top, the sides long sinews of carved and knotted wood. There was a little bit of fluff stuck in the crevice at the top. I tried to pick it out with my fingernail. Fuschia walked past and seeing what I was doing burst into a fit of laughter, holding her hand to her mouth and scuttling away, her espadrilles flapping on the floor tiles. I didn't see what was so funny. I stepped back and looked at the statue. It reminded me of something I couldn't place.

With Fuschia gone, I inspected the room. There were two white-leather sofas, grouped around a glass coffee table, on which there was a bronze statue of a naked lady arching backwards in a moment of pure ecstasy. The smooth wooden table gleamed and smelt of polish. There was a side unit with drawers and cupboards which smelt of beeswax, housing a collection of spirits that would have satisfied even the Ifor Evans rugby team. A robin bobbed across the neatly trimmed lawn, stopping to rest beneath a plum tree, its branches laden with fruit.

It was impossible to imagine that Paris lay somewhere over the horizon. It might as well have been a million miles away.

I sat on the edge of the cold, white sofa without feeling the slightest bit at home. This was nothing like the neat bungalow on the estate where I had grown up. The footprint of my childhood home would have fitted comfortably inside the dining room alone. But for all its grandeur, I wasn't sure I liked it. There wasn't a TV for a start. And the sofas were too cold to imagine curling up on and reading a book.

Above my head came the sound of rhythmic tapping on the stairs. Madame Blanchard coming down on her crutches? I sprung to the middle of the room, standing to attention as if I'd been waiting there since sunrise.

Madame Blanchard swung into the room with surprising agility.

'*Bonjour, Karen, heureuse de vous rencontrer enfin.*'

She kissed me on each cheek, then settled herself down, propping her crutches up on the side of the white sofa. Of all the different Florence Blanchards I had imagined, none had looked like this. She had a sweet, angelic face, without a trace of make-up on her clear skin. Her dark eyebrows were unplucked and framed her dark-brown eyes. Her hair was tied back into a long plait which tapered all the way down her spine to her waist. It was knotted with a simple elastic band like a schoolgirl. She was wearing a blue, strappy T-shirt which clung to her flat breasts, revealing the hollow of her breast bone: a 'no bra' kind of woman. Her trousers were ethnic and baggy; the sort of outfit only a very thin woman could wear. Her naked arms were long and muscly, and there was a shocking sprout of black hair visible in the hollow of her armpit. Her hand, as she reached out to clasp mine, had well-defined, strong fingers; short nails, no varnish. There was nothing Yves Saint Laurent or Chanel about Madame Blanchard. Her smile was kind and reassuring.

Florence Blanchard told me that she spoke and understood English perfectly, but that after I'd settled in she would only speak French to me, 'so that you may learn'. She also reminded me that of her three children, Delphine, Baptiste and Clémence, only Delphine could speak a little English, having spent her early years in America.

Florence – as she told me to call her – sighed and gave what I would come to recognise as her worried look.

'I'm afraid Delphine is a little difficult,' she said. 'She is struggling with the idea of yet another *jeune fille au pair*. She feels that now she is eleven years old, she is big enough to manage without one.'

'Oh, I see,' I said, feeling worried. 'So, how do you think she'll react when she sees me then?'

'*Je ne sais pas*,' laughed Florence. 'Last time she cracked eggs in the poor girl's shoes and played so many other tricks she turned my hair grey. But she is a good girl, and she will grow to love you, *n'est-ce pas?*'

Florence surveyed the room and then brought her eyes back to rest on me. She looked me up and down. I was wearing a baggy blue and white pin-striped dress, bought from my favourite shop in Aberystwyth: Lettuce and Melbury. The shop specialised in vintage materials sold at extortionate prices. Far from the clutches of Cassie and her black leggings brigade, I'd reverted to type, with a suitcase full of romantic dresses. The stripes lent, what I hoped, was a kind of Mary Poppins appeal to my outfit. Of course, I'd also brought an array of sexy black underwear, bought from Marks and Spencer's, lingering with intent in my bedroom drawer. I intended to wage my own religious war on David, as soon as I found him.

My mind had been wandering but Florence was talking, an earnest look engraved upon her Madonna-like face.

'To find the right girl is very important for us,' she said, reminding me why I was sitting on her sofa. 'I have my work, and my husband is very involved in his own.'

'Oh, do you work?' I asked, surprised. I couldn't imagine Florence in an office.

'I am an artist,' she said, 'and most days I am busy with my sculptures.' She indicated the self-pleasuring woman and the wooden statue to indicate that this was her work. I understood better why her fingers were so strong.

'Oh, how lovely,' I said, 'I particularly like the wooden one. What does it represent?'

Florence smiled a wry little smile, her head on one side. 'It is a phallus,' she said. 'How do you say … ? A penis.'

I remembered Fuschia's laughter as I'd plucked fur balls from the crack.

Florence smiled. 'I am working hard for my next exhibition,' she said, 'and I'm working in bronze. I've just bought a studio, in an old biscuit factory, which I'm having renovated. It is not ready yet, though most days I'm out, overseeing the works. Until this of course!' She laughed, revealing a neat row of teeth and pale gums, pointing to her leg which she raised slightly, to show me that normally she was both graceful and athletic. 'And my husband,' she continued, 'is – how shall I put it? – very *important* in business.'

I widened my eyes with a look of interest, though I cared nothing about business.

'Yes, he is a very influential man,' Florence laughed, 'or so everyone tells me. This week there was an article on him in a very prominent journal.'

'Oh, he's famous then!' I said.

'Well, if the world of business interests you, then yes,' said Florence, dismissively. 'We do not share the same love of art of course. He thinks of it as my little, how shall I say, foible? Yes, he sees it as my foible. A whim, if you prefer.'

'Oh, and art is everything, isn't it,' I said, waving my hand in the air as if batting a fly.

I wanted to keep on the right side of my new employer – both employers – and yet I sensed a vague thrill of disloyalty towards Monsieur Blanchard coursing through my veins.

Florence graced me with her delicate smile. 'To me, yes, my husband and my children are everything. But we women must forge time for our creative selves, *n'est-ce pas?*'

'Oh, absolutely.'

'Then today you shall meet some artists,' smiled Florence

brightly, 'I'm having a *déjeuner* with Hugo and Marcel.'

'Hugo? The artist who painted this?' I asked, pointing to the abstract storm brewing on the wall of the otherwise neat and tidy salon.

'Yes, how clever of you. Hugo is a great painter, and Marcel ... well Marcel is a very talented architect. That is also art of a kind, *n'est-ce pas*? He is very modest; he plays the piano so well. And it is he who is designing my *atelier*, a room for me to seek refuge in, far from the world. They are coming here today. You can cook a little light lunch for us perhaps? *Rien de compliqué.*'

Hawk talons of panic pierced my heart. I hadn't cooked since the days of powdered mashed potato and frozen fish fingers with Cassie. There had been no need since that run on free curries up at Cwrt Mawr, when food appeared magically on my plate every evening, after long afternoons of blissful love-making. Where was Rafi with his big saucepans of bubbling dal when you needed him? Had the advert said anything about cooking? Hmmm. There had been some mention of tasty meals. After only half a day, I was about to come unstuck.

Thankfully, Florence, appearing to sense my terror, smiled and patted my arm.

'I will help you,' she said kindly, 'until you find your way.' Florence swung into the kitchen, and I trailed in shadow behind her. Watching her work, I saw that this was clearly a woman who knew her kitchen inside out, though she had a house full of domestic helpers. She displayed an immediate and evident talent for housewifery and cooking, while sending out the clear message that none of these tasks were *her* responsibility.

My new boss was the first in a line of French women I would meet over the years, all of whom operated a military regime in the kitchen and who believed that *their* way was the *only* way to do things.

Florence propped up her sticks, swinging from worksurface to worksurface, clunking a heavy frying pan onto the hob and spraying it with olive oil from a small, silver pump. Four succulent lamb chops were thrown in. They sizzled in their juices while she snipped fresh rosemary from a branch and sprinkled it over the meat with a twist of sea salt and pepper. She prepared a pan of boiling water for the runner beans which she topped and tailed with deft, muscular fingers; fingers used to squeezing clay and pressing it into phallic shapes all day. Fingers which seemed to say there was somewhere else they'd rather be, engaging in less *menial* duties. Her nails were clipped short and unvarnished in a clearly no-nonsense manner. The pink nail varnish I'd painted on my own nails, for my new life in Paris, had started to flake and I longed to remove it. A long strand of her hair trailed down Florence's face and she smiled and pinned it back up. Her face was young without make-up. I admired her translucid skin and those light-brown eyelashes, uncluttered by the gunky mascara that clogged my own. She took a yellow Moroccan bowl from a cupboard and tore strips of fresh spinach leaves into it, adding thin slices of chopped shallot and preparing a vinaigrette with such vigour that the muscles on her arms stood out.

I watched awkwardly, not knowing what to do, sensing

I was underfoot. Florence, who was clearly thinking the same thing, told me to go and set the table. '*Quatre places. Toi, Marcel, Hugo et moi.* The plates are in the cupboard in the dining room.'

I found everything in a neatly arranged cupboard and set the places. Florence called through to put out both wine and water glasses, and I made an educated guess at which one to put where. We'd always drunk tea with our meals at home, never wine, especially not at lunchtime.

The doorbell rang and Florence asked me to carry the food through while she swung up the hallway to open the door and welcome her guests.

Deep voices filled the entrance hall. When she returned, Florence's pale skin was flushed. The two men who towered above her in height flanked her sides like bodyguards. Hugo was exactly as I'd expected from his turbulent artwork: broad-shouldered and arrogant-looking, with a mass of swirling black hair. He kissed the air to each side of my cheek, looking visibly displeased at my presence. Although I didn't understand what he was saying, I knew that he had immediately dismissed me as a domestic and sensed a prick of pride at the memory of the degree certificate rolled up in my case. I wasn't *really* a servant of course. I was a graduate; an expert in Middle English and the Norse sagas. American Literature and the Romantic poets. This wasn't forever. I was masquerading as a nanny in the name of true love, only to keep a roof over my head. But Hugo, who neither knew this nor cared, handed me his jacket and pushed past.

Despite the warm spring weather, Marcel was wearing a trilby hat à la Humphrey Bogart. He took it off, bowed and then kissed me on each cheek; a kiss moist enough to lift a microparticle of blusher. His eyes met mine and held my gaze. With *Marcel*, I existed. He didn't look as if he expected me to clean his shoes. His smile was the charming, slanted kind, with a sharp canine tooth which protruded slightly over his lip leaving a small indentation in the flesh. He reminded me of a cat.

Back in the salon, Florence had come over all faint with her exertions, and the two men busied themselves by pulling up a chair, sitting her down, and relieving her of her crutches so that we could begin our meal. I wondered why they didn't rub her feet. Marcel uncorked the wine. The conversation was in English for my benefit. Only Hugo, who spoke very little, barked an unapologetic stream of French, staring at Florence the whole time. I realised how difficult it was to grasp the French language when it was spoken quickly, and by someone who lacked the patience of a lover. Rapid-fire Parisian French always sounds pissed off. I longed to be back in David's arms, practising the few phrases I knew off by heart: *Je t'aime; Tu me manques; Embrasse-moi.*

A wave of sadness swept over me. The tiredness of the journey, the exhaustion of having to smile for hours on end in a strange house, and now, worse still, trying to look interested when I hadn't a clue what was being said. If only I could go back to my hessian-clad room, and crawl into the architectural equivalent of an art teacher's bag.

Marcel seemed to pick up on a little of my sadness

and caught my eye with his own bright-blue inquisitive stare. He winked, cast a quick glance at Florence and Hugo who were consumed in a heated discussion, and sucked a runner bean in through the side of his mouth while crossing his eyes. I smiled, and he scrunched a blink of acknowledgement. He had a kind face.

After cheese and more wine, all of which was handed out in a matter-of-fact way as though this was regular lunchtime fare, and a closing ceremony of lip-dabbing with crisp linen napkins, Florence stood up and nodded in the direction of the salon. Hugo and Marcel rose to their feet and pushed back their chairs. I prepared to follow the party to the white-leather sofa. 'Can you prepare the coffee?' Florence asked, intercepting me with her crutch. It was a gentle, soul-destroying reminder of my role in the household. Of course, they wanted some time alone amongst friends now.

Frustratingly, coffee, surely the simplest of tasks to demand of a new employee, proved yet another challenge. My mother drank milky coffee laced with a dash of brandy on frosty mornings, or when she was in shock at one of my dad's latest antics; but hers was the instant stuff from screw-top jars involving none of the paraphernalia with which I was now faced.

Florence's was a *real* coffee machine, requiring the use of filters and ground coffee. I wondered if I could cheat, and scanned the shelves for a jar of instant, but to no avail. The Chinese gunpowder sat in stubborn solitude.

I lifted the lid of the coffee machine and saw that there were two parts to the inner body of the machine.

The top part was curved and grooved, and surely the correct recipient for the filter. I found the box of filters, blessing the manufacturer who had had the good sense to draw pictures on the boxes for non-French-speaking customers, and placed one inside. So far so good. Next to the machine there was a jar of strong ground coffee, with a little plastic scoop just like the ones used to measure out powder for baby milk. As there were four of us, I calculated that eight scoops of ground coffee should be about right – with an extra three for the pot. The only remaining issue was where to put the water. I hastily filled the jug from the tap and poured it in onto the coffee and pressed the button. *Voilà*! I was a pleased French housewife in the western suburbs of Paris about to serve strong black coffee to my guests!

The machine glugged and spluttered while I took out the cups and saucers. Florence called to me to bring chocolates from the fridge. When I returned, the water had trickled right through into the Perspex carafe. I touched it gently knowing it might scald but it was stone-cold. Not only this but the water was completely colourless. The coffee grains hadn't released their essence into the water, or turned hot, or into anything vaguely resembling coffee. I wanted to grab the moist bundle and squeeze it hard into the water, but what would be the point? This still wouldn't qualify as a hot drink.

Why couldn't they teach coffee-making to grumpy French artists and their friends in Home Economics lessons at school? All those hours wasted learning about eggs and protein, and I couldn't make a jug of coffee. I cursed my family for buying instant coffee all those years, and cursed myself for not having added a coffee percolator to my list of engagement presents with Steve. But Steve's family had only drunk tea – tea and beer.

'*Ça va, là-dedans?*' Florence called, with a hint of impatience.

'*Ça va bien!*' I replied, willing her not to hobble in.

I weighed up the situation. There were only two possible places the water could go. I must have chosen the wrong one. I took out the wet filter and stuffed it into the bin, and started again, this time pouring the water into the side vents, wondering the whole time how, with the coffee and the water separated in this manner, the two would ever meet.

I was as relieved as if I'd delivered one of Madame Blanchard's children, when minutes later with much gurgling and glugging, a jet of hot coffee gushed into the jug. I returned proudly to the salon balancing the coffee jug on a tray. *Naturellement* the coffee was too strong, and Hugo spat it back out into his cup in disgust.

'*Fuck! What is this shit?*'

So, he could speak English after all.

Marcel politely drained his cup and swallowed with a slight shake of the head, grabbing a black chocolate from the bowl and knocking it to the back of his throat like an aspirin. Florence put her cup down and sucked on the end of her spoon.

'*Ma chèrie,*' she said, 'why don't you do some ironing now. This is usually what the *au pair* girls do until it is time to collect the children from school. Fuschia will accompany you today as they do not know you, and I cannot walk so well.'

Florence explained that Fuschia had set up their ironing board in the basement, and that I would find the stairs to the lower level at the end of the hallway.

Dismissed, I left the room in time to hear Hugo mutter something beneath his breath which set the other two off laughing.

Red-faced, I located the door to the cellar half-hidden behind a coat-rack, and clicked on the light. The steps curved downwards into the smell of warm leather. The stone stairwell was littered with pairs of boots and trainers. Wicker baskets of sprouting potatoes nestled in the dark, next to bicycle pumps and various other objects: a skateboard, straw hats on pegs, an old gardening coat, and other paraphernalia from the Blanchard household. I followed the winding stairs downwards to the cellar; deep into the bowels of the family home.

Here, beneath the house, a network of pipes ran across the ceilings and along the wall from the boiler. I touched one. It was boiling hot. The room smelt, not unpleasantly, of engine oil; the same smell Dad carried on his white work overalls when he came home from the airport. It made me want to cry. A single light bulb flickered on. It was a strangely warm and comforting refuge, like a nest or a submarine, far removed from the upstairs world of domesticity and orders.

In my dreams, I'd considered climbing the Eiffel Tower in Paris, holding David's hand, or dancing like

Fred Astaire and Ginger Rogers down the Champs Elysées. Instead, for now at least, I was happy to be in a basement room, somewhere west of Paris, far from the sound of Hugo's sarcastic laugh.

I thought about all the other *jeune fille au pair* who had stood here: au pairs with eggs in their shoes, or salt in their tea instead of sugar. There was an old radio hanging on a hook on the wall. I switched it on. To my surprise, Radio 4 crackled out. It was Jenny Murray – *Woman's Hour*.

The girl before me must have been English too, and I slipped into her place. The crackling and whistling signal wasn't good, but still it felt like home. The water pipes babbled and the boiler clicked on.

I leant against the ironing board and considered the immense pile of washing in the basket. Just as I feared, the first thing to greet me was a pair of Axel Blanchard's underpants. It seemed strange to consider them. They were blue and red, and slightly ridiculous with jaunty white sailing boats around the waistband. I imagined how they lay beneath his sober suit the whole day, while he sat in board-meetings wearing the secret flamboyant pants that no-one saw; no-one except Florence, and now me. As I started to sort the clothes from the basket I thought of my best friend Scarlett who would be in Milan by now, starting work at her new language school. I wasn't sure when I'd see Paris or be given a day off or manage to attend the French lessons I'd enrolled in at l'Institut Catholique on the rue de Rennes. Wherever that was.

I arranged a mountain of socks into pairs, realising that

socks were the same the world over: grey and worn at the heel, and most often bereft of a partner – it didn't matter how big in business you were, or how many articles there were written about you in magazines. There was usually a potato in your heel.

After a time, the folding became therapeutic: sorting out the lives of others before I could begin my own. I was familiar with the children's clothing before meeting them, sensing the personality behind Clémence's girlish princess pinks or Delphine's green tomboy jerseys, almost indistinguishable from Baptiste's own.

The radio crackled out a travel piece on cruises. I imagined the pounding of the sea in the glugging pipes above my head, safe in my warm and oily submarine.

I closed my eyes, lost in thought, until with a shiver I sensed I might no longer be alone. I was not.

There was a shadow on the wall of a trilby hat. Beneath it, the broad-shouldered form of a man. It was Marcel. He moved down the stairs and across the room to the ironing board, ducking beneath the low ceiling and pipes. Surfacing before me, he removed his hat and gave a theatrical bow.

Then, before I had time to comprehend, he kissed me gently, stepped back, replaced his hat and smiled.

'*Au revoir, mademoiselle*,' he said, and was gone, bounding up the stone steps, two at a time.

CHAPTER 6

A few minutes before four o'clock, an alarm clock, positioned on the water pipes above my head, let out a shrill ring. I pressed the off button and heard the door at the top of the cellar steps grind open. Fuschia's thick, homely legs appeared step by step, as she padded down in her worn espadrilles.

I had been ironing for two hours, pounding hot metal onto cuffs and collars, turning the children's sweatshirts inside out as I learnt the hard way, that the images stuck to the bottom of the iron if you didn't. Lost in thought to the crackle of my radio (and except for one interruption involving an architect in a trilby) I'd blotted out the world upstairs. Surely I wouldn't have to meet these unruly, eggbreaking children, let alone take care of them.

The idea of my taking care of three children seemed suddenly absurd. Children were an unknown species to me. I didn't as yet have a maternal bone in my body.

These would grow later.

I consoled myself that in a few weeks, once I'd found David, I'd be gone. This was a temporary blip.

Fuschia approached the ironing board, the shadow of her bulky frame rising before me. One of Axel's socks, hanging on the line above her head, tickled the top of her turban.

'*C'est l'heure de l'école. On y va?*'

She smiled encouragingly and pointed to the clock.

I knew what she was saying: it was school-time; time to meet my wards. But my feet had rooted to the floor.

'*On y va,*' I said, with a heavy heart.

We clanged the wrought-iron gate shut and set off. Fuschia was wearing a light rain-coat over a colourful, long green dress that matched her turban. She carried a black bag which she swung jauntily. It was enormous, and looked more like an old briefcase than a handbag. One of Axel's cast-offs perhaps?

Outside the school gates a determined crowd had gathered and was waiting with intent. Mothers stared anxiously at the gates. I was at a disadvantage as I didn't know who I was looking for and didn't want to rush up and hug the wrong children. There weren't any men present, unless you counted the policeman brandishing the STOP sign on the zebra crossing.

The other mothers were quick to check me out. This was a French habit which would become familiar over the years: a hard stare from top to bottom and back up again, taking in every item of clothing, breast size and hair style. A woman with a pushchair nudged her friend and said with a disparaging look: '*Une jeune fille au pair.*'

The two women were dressed neatly in prim blue dresses and those kitten-heel shoes suitable for church on Sundays. Both women were wearing scarves, Hermès no doubt.

At the back of the crowd two tall blonde girls were laughing and speaking loudly in a language which wasn't French. German perhaps? Or Dutch?

They must have been au pairs too. The crowd was divided into women who had given birth and were waiting for their progeny, and those who hadn't but were living the experience at the expense of their host families.

The gates opened, and a swarm of children emerged, laden down with huge satchels on their backs. One boy, who looked about six, was bent double. Surely, he couldn't have *that* much homework. There wasn't a single child without a heavy bag strapped to its back like paramilitary army kit. The locker concept had not hit France, nor was it endorsed over the years, to protect children from spinal strain, despite yearly articles of woe from paediatricians.

The children wore the solemn look of wartime refugees in their neat shorts and socks. They did not wear school uniforms and yet their clothes were less colourful and childlike than the clothes of English children; there were fewer Disney motifs or cutesy anthropomorphic mice. Most were dressed as miniature adults. Later I learnt this was very 'western suburbs of Paris': the plaid skirts for girls in traditional blues and greens; the neat little shirts and shorts for the boys – all procured from shops such as *Cyrillus* or *Tartine et Chocolat*. Though Florence was far from traditional herself, her children were turned out in keeping with her class and social situation.

A skinny, blonde girl with fine straight hair skidded to a halt in front of Fuschia and kissed her on the cheek. Her pale almond eyes were perfectly set in a heart-shaped face.

There was no mistaking her angelic features. Clémence was every inch her mother's child.

I knew, from the application in *The Lady* magazine that she was six years old, but she checked me out from top to bottom, as if I was being assessed for the position by the head of Human Resources.

'*Je suis Clémence*,' she said, sweetly but knowingly, as if aware of her charms. I felt her small hand as it slipped into mine.

Fuschia prodded me and pointed to the railings near the park. A taller version of Clémence scowled by the gate in the shadow of an oak.

'*Et voici ma sœur*,' Clémence said, pointing to her sister, '*elle s'appelle Delphine*.'

I was wondering whether to go over to Delphine and say hello, when a dark-haired boy with a mass of black curly hair bounced up and threw his bag down, almost breaking my toe. His face hadn't yet grown to accommodate his new teeth, lending him a toothy, cheeky look. His dark brown eyes, with their thick brush lashes, and his full rosebud lips, would break hearts one day.

He kissed me hard on the cheek, almost knocking me over. I wasn't entirely comfortable with all this hand-holding and cheek-kissing. My family wasn't tactile at the best of times.

'*Je suis Baptiste*,' he said.

The set of three was complete: Clémence, holding my hand; Baptiste, charming as hell and looking nothing like his father; and Delphine, sulking.

To my alarm, Fuschia raised her hand to bid us *au revoir* and headed off towards the station, her oversized espadrilles flapping the pavement.

I wondered in panic if I could remember the way home, but Clémence (I could *almost* kiss her) liked to take charge and pulled me down the street. Baptiste followed by my side, head down as he shuffled a pack of cards. I looked behind and saw that Delphine was following us. She was tall and angular, much like her father. She stuck out her tongue.

Clémence explained: '*Elle pense qu'elle est assez grande pour rentrer seule.*' The youngest girl was right. Her elder sister *was* big enough to walk home by herself and had every reason to sulk. To be honest she looked more capable than I was. I felt a little afraid of her.

Back at the house the plates from lunchtime were piled neatly by the kitchen sink, unwashed. I gathered these were waiting for me, and I felt a prick of annoyance that while I'd been busy ironing and picking up her kids, Florence hadn't thought to wash up.

The children ran around the kitchen pulling open doors, extracting boxes of breakfast cereal, banging milk onto the table, and taking out packets of cheese and jars of jam. There was half a baguette left from lunchtime which they tore into pieces like hyenas. I watched in amazement. This was easy. The children were making their own dinner! Clémence opened the coffee cupboard and took out a tablet of chocolate, breaking it into three chunks, which she distributed so that each child could insert a piece into their morsel of bread.

'*Pain au chocolat*,' Baptiste explained, with his mouth full. I sat down and watched. Delphine had cut herself a chunk of cheese which she spread with cherry jam. She spoke in rapid French to her brother and sister without looking at me, and I was certain she was speaking quickly so that I wouldn't understand.

Florence must still be resting. I hadn't seen her since lunchtime. I knew Marcel had left (my stomach lurched at the thought of his secret goodbye kiss), but had Moody Hugo gone? Surely, he wouldn't be lurking upstairs with Axel Blanchard due home so soon – even if he was a friend. I couldn't imagine any of the men I knew being pleased to return home after a hard day at the office, to find a glowering hulk of a man in their private chambers.

The gates outside creaked open. I looked through the window and saw a grey-haired lady wheeling in an enormous bicycle. The wicker basket at the front was piled high with shopping.

'Mamie!' Clémence screamed, throwing her head back and spreading her arms out rigidly as if she was having a fit. She ran to open the door, while I brushed myself down.

The lady parked her bike by the hedge and attached a metal chain. With her neat grey bun, tweed skirt and jacket, tan tights (despite the warm weather) and sensible shoes, she looked as if she was off to audition for the part of Miss Marple.

I opened the door, and she held out a bag of *croissants* and *pains au chocolat*. I took the bag and shook her hand. 'I'm Bonne-Maman,' she said, which was clearly not just jam with a pretty patterned lid, but a way of addressing grandmothers, 'the mother of Florence. I am come to see how you are settling in and how my daughter is doing.'

The children's grandmother, who told me her name was Françoise, took immediate possession of the kitchen in much the same way as her daughter had at lunchtime. She cast a disapproving look at the pile of food in the middle of the table, the puddle of milk slopped out of its carton, the cheese wrappers and dirty knives, the pat of butter streaked with jam.

Bonne-Maman stripped off her tweed jacket, and rolled up the sleeves of her turquoise chemise, barking out orders until, within minutes, the kitchen table had been tidied with military precision. The food was not put away, but rearranged tidily on the table, with small plates, knives and plastic beakers. I gathered that I was at fault for allowing the children to eat like pigs at a trough. Once satisfied, Françoise distributed her pastries and offered me the last *pain au chocolat*.

'To keep you strong,' she said, 'we don't want you having a *malaise* like the last girl.'

It was clear from the old woman's tone that my strength

must be kept up not for *my* benefit, but to ensure that I remained strong and ox-like to preserve Florence's own health. She filled a glass full of milk, and insisted I drink it. I wasn't used to the French habit of drinking sterilised milk, gagging at its latent odour, but she waited until I had drunk the whole glass as if I was one of the children. She was fattening me up like a Russian peasant, so I could better plough the fields. Soon she would be checking the density of my bones.

I was surprised that French dinner was so pastry-orientated. I had imagined meats and vegetables, but it was a huge relief. Even I could manage dinners like this one. I had been worried it would be snails, rabbit, or offal.

Once we had finished the children were sent to their rooms to complete their homework. Even Clémence had a colouring project which she had to finish. Bonne-Maman sat at the table and watched me tidy up.

'Soon it is *les grandes vacances* and I will be taking you to Trémouillet,' she said. 'It is where we always spend *la Toussaint* in autumn, and a fortnight in the summer, before we go down to Aix-en-Provence to open up the house there.'

It was the first I've heard of a trip away and I'd no idea where Trémouillet was. I'd forgotten the school year was ending soon, and that the children would shortly be a permanent fixture in my life. No more solitary ironing in The Submarine.

'*C'est où ça?*' I asked in my best French.

'Trémouillet is not a town,' she said in English, 'it is the family château. Sadly, we are not able to go there so often, but the guardian and his wife, Monsieur et Madame Villard, manage it perfectly.'

'You own a château you don't live in?'

'Our lives are in Paris, but the children enjoy it in the holidays. It is a pretty place with a moat. Medieval in origin. You will be most fulfilled. There is a large kitchen for the preparation of jams and foods.'

She looked at me expectantly.

'We have copper pans for the preparation of cherry jam and other jellies. And *bien évidemment* there will be the *courgettes* and *aubergines* to make ratatouille for winter. In autumn there will be mushrooms to collect, and we will teach you to identify those which make a good omelette with garlic from the "Trumpets of Death".'

Did Bonne-Maman really imagine I'd be bottling jams and stocking up the winter pantry?

'Will Florence and Axel be coming?' I asked quickly.

Only they knew the exact terms of my contract.

She laughed.

'*Mais non*. Axel has much work to do and Florence is busy with her *atelier*. I take the children in the holidays every summer, before I must hand them over to Mamie'. She saw my look of confusion. 'I am Bonne-Maman Françoise, and the *other* grandmother is Mamie Colette. The mother of Axel.' She said this with a sniff and shake of her head.

'And where does Mamie Colette live?' I asked.

'She lives in Paris,' the old woman said, shaking her head, 'at the foot of the *Tour Eiffel*. Never will she leave the city. She does not know the joy of mushroom picking or hunting for deer in open air. For her a truffle is something you order *Chez Fauchon*, whereas at the château, we have our own pigs to root for them and woods grown especially for the truffles that were planted by my grandfather. *Des truffières.*'

She leant towards me and peered into my eyes conspiratorially. 'My daughter's husband, how do you say this?'

'Your son-in-law?'

'Yes, my son-in-law, that's right. Well, the mother of my son-in-law, she has never washed her hair by herself.'

She laughed and sat back as if to better gauge my reaction.

'What, never, in all her life?' 'No! Not once. Not ever.' 'But that's disgusting.'

The woman shook her head. 'You do not understand me. She has never washed her hair *herself*, nor has she ever boiled an egg. She has domestics who do it for her.'

'What, everything?'

'*Parfaitement.* They cook and clean and wash her hair. And if she wants a boiled egg they boil it. The whole house is full of people *like you.*'

'Like me?'

'*Mais oui. Les domestiques.* The servants.'

Bonne-Maman ran her fingers across her neat bun and pinned back a lock of stray hair. 'I may not have so many *servants*,' she said, 'at least not here in Paris, but my hair is clean. And I can shoot and fish, pluck the feathers from a pheasant, and make pâté with the liver of a duck.

Mamie, she knows none of this. She only drinks tea while her husband lies dying in the back bedroom. He has been dying now for nearly twenty years. My husband, he died in one month. There is no need for such a fuss. But you will see her for yourself, *ma petite*, soon you will see her for yourself.'

Bonne-Maman stood up and pushed her chair back to the table.

'You need to wash the children now,' she said, 'I will say hello to Florence. Is she in her bedroom alone?'

'Yes. I think so.'

'It is always best to check these things,' she said, 'one should never assume.'

CHAPTER 7

Clémence and Delphine were wet-haired from their bath. Their afterschool routine was so well engrained that they'd ploughed on in my absence. They'd laid out their school clothes for the next day, packed their bags and lined up their dirty shoes outside the bedroom door.

'The shoes are for you to polish,' Delphine said coldly, in English. She barely looked up from combing her sister's hair as I popped my head round the door. I watched her as she fastened a pair of neat, cherry-red slides on each side of her sister's parting. Delphine's look was serious and maternal. More maternal than her own mother perhaps, who lounged upstairs in the great unknown quarters of the eastern wing and hadn't seen the children since they'd returned from school. Clémence was a prettier child than her sister, who had a gaunt and worried look. Delphine and I had still not exchanged a single word of pleasantry. '*Tu me trouves belle?*' Clémence asked, peering into the mirror and stroking her golden locks.

I smiled. '*Oui Clémence, très belle.* You are very beautiful.' Both girls were wearing long nightshirts of thick, sensible cotton. I was surprised at how early they went to bed. The sun hadn't set, and there was a misty haze hanging over the city of Paris, visible on the horizon from the upstairs window. I longed to go to the heart of the city. For now, I was trapped in this house, part of this family, and without even the money for a metro ticket.

Baptiste was in the corner of the room, still dressed in his green jumper and check shorts, playing with a train.

I laid a hand on his shoulder and pointed to the bathroom. He shrugged me off and ignored me. Clémence said something which I didn't understand.

'You must wash him; he never takes his bath alone.'

It was Delphine who had spoken once again, in perfect English with a hint of American.

'Your English is so good,' I said, hoping a little flattery wouldn't go amiss. It worked with Clémence, who had been all smiles since I'd praised her looks. Delphine ignored me and continued to work on her sister's hair.

'Delphine, could you ask Baptiste to take his bath now, please?' I asked, in a firm voice.

'You tell him,' she snapped. 'You're here to learn French.'

Clémence, who had divined the problem, jumped down from the bed and grabbed the train from her brother.

Within seconds the two were screaming and fighting, as Baptiste pulled one of the red hair clips from his sister's hair which by now was as matted as the first Mrs Rochester's. Clémence kicked and screamed, but Baptiste back-flipped her to the ground and sat on her pressing so hard on her neck she turned Smurf blue. Delphine looked on from her bedside position with a smug smile that said: 'Sort that one out, if you can.'

Bonne-Maman appeared at the door on cue and pulled the two combatants apart. Clémence, who had retreated into the corner of her bedroom like a Sumo wrestler in the wing, preparing for the next round, was dragging oxygen into her lungs with great noisy rasps. Bonne-Maman ordered me to take Baptiste to the bathroom to wash his hair and *tout son corps*.

I ran the bath and Baptiste climbed in. I averted my eyes not knowing where to look. Baptiste seemed too old to be washed by a stranger, but his grandmother was adamant. He stared silently into the running water, still sulking at not having properly throttled Clémence.

'*Il faut me laver les cheveux,*' he said, repeating Bonne Maman's instructions to wash his hair.

I squeezed a blob of shampoo onto his thick black locks and he squeaked as the cold liquid hit his warm crown.

'*Pardon.*'

There was a jug on the side of the tub which I filled with warm bath water, rubbing the top of his head. He ignored me completely. I tapped him on the shoulder and motioned to him to close his eyes while I rinsed. He closed his thick, doe-like lashes obediently. Hopefully we were nearly finished. It hadn't been too bad after all. I'd just grabbed a big fluffy towel from the radiator, when Bonne-Maman loomed upon us again.

'*Vous avez lavé ses fesses?*'

Seeing my puzzled expression she reverted to English. 'Have you washed his ass?' The word shocked me. Bonne-Maman must have seen a lot of American TV to have picked up such language.

I didn't know what to say. I'd never washed anyone's ass except my own. It was a horrible thought akin to changing a nappy. Maybe I was too English around the edges, but all this body contact with strangers was making me uncomfortable. It wasn't as if I'd trained as a nurse. There had been no mention of bum washing in the job description.

Bonne-Maman's back was turned as she mechanically rearranged towels in the airing cupboard. I was thankful for small mercies. It was bad enough having to do the job in the first place, without her beady eyes on me. I reached for the shower gel and poured it into the palm of my hand. Baptiste was driving the sponge up and down the edge of the bath, revving and tooting, lost in a world of his own. He seemed younger than his years. I cast my eyes to the ceiling and dived my hand down into the depths of the water, in the vague direction of his crotch, hoping that a quick splash of water would suffice back and front. I knew I hadn't *touched* anything, but surely the hot water would have washed him?

To my horror, Baptiste threw his sponge across

the bathroom, hitting his grandmother between the shoulder blades and leaving a wet patch on her turquoise blouse. He started to scream. Bonne-Maman spun around; a whirr of tan tights.

'*Mais qu'est-ce que vous faites?*' she thundered, a look of horror etched on her walnut face.

Baptiste was screaming but there were words now too: '*Elle a touché mon zizi.*' He pointed down into the murky waters as if he'd been stung by a jellyfish.

Bonne-Maman stared at me as if I'd just crawled up from the drains.

'He says you have touched his private area. His manhood,' She was all fire and indignation.

I flushed scarlet, 'No! I don't think so. I mean I'm sure not. Not on purpose at least, even if I did, God forbid. Anyway, I thought that was what you wanted me to do?'

'With your *hand*,' she reiterated, 'he says you have touched his *zizi* with your *hand*.'

'Well, how else was I to wash him?' I was at a complete loss, visions of dismissal for inappropriate behaviour whizzing through my mind.

'With a *glove* of course,' she said firmly.

A glove? The woman was mad? She wanted me to wash his bum with a glove?

Seeing my confusion, Bonne-Maman reached across to the sink and picked up a piece of square cloth. She rinsed it in the water and slipped her hand inside. It was a rectangle no bigger than the size of her hand, consisting of two pieces of material sewn together.

'This,' she said, flapping the square cloth at my face,

'is a glove. *Un gant*. It is placed on the hand to wash. It exfoliates, and it saves the poor boy from embarrassment. This is the way we do things in France. *Oh là là. Ces anglaises!*'

Bonne-Maman sailed off into the night on her clanging bicycle. I was sitting at the bottom of the stairs cleaning shoes: three pairs of soiled and muddy school shoes, to be precise. There was a cream polish for each: white, for Baptiste's trainers; black for Delphine's sandals; and red for Clémence's.

The day felt never-ending.

After Baptiste's bathtime, Clémence had led me by the hand to a cupboard beneath the stairs where she had pointed to a wooden box of bristle brushes and cloths, before rushing upstairs to join her brother and sister

If the children went to bed this early every night, I'd be able to go into town. I just needed to ask Florence for an advance on my wages. If I ever saw her again. The house had swallowed her up and I'd been relegated to the kitchen and the nursery. I wasn't confident enough yet to seek her out in her private quarters.

I'd never had to clean shoes before. I squirted liquid erratically at clods of earth. My shoes never seemed to get so dirty back at university. If they did, I'd wash them off in the sea. Sometimes in Aberystwyth sand would collect inside them that I'd tip out into a little pyramid on to the hall floors. But never mud. Not like *this*. The shoe polish stuck to the wads of earth. Looking into the box, and seeing the wire brushes, it occurred to me that perhaps I should have scrubbed them first.

I was Cinderella sitting on the steps polishing shoes that smelt of other people's feet. I had no money, and unlike the children, who had stuffed their faces with pints of milk and wads of Emmental cheese topped with juicy strawberry jam, I had only half a pain au chocolat in my stomach and was hungry. I was starting to feel resentful. Where *was* Florence anyway? I'd done nothing but iron in a barely ventilated cellar filled with oil fumes, wash children and scrub shoes. The only word of French I'd learnt was *poubelle*. Clémence had taught me as she held out a snotty tissue and pointed to the dustbin. She wanted me to put it inside – and so whenever I said the word *poubelle* for the rest of my French life, I remembered dainty little Clémence. She had already learnt about human bondage and slavery, and at the ripe old age of six, already knew that I came beneath her in the pecking order. Clémence of the 'full glasses of sterilised milk' and the 'healthy froth around the lips'; Clémence with her red hair slides and those innocent pale brown eyes who was blissfully unaware of the agonies of love, or shoe cleaning. I was sure that if David and I had children, I wouldn't want some other woman poking around in my house, observing my every mood. Why couldn't Florence take care of her own children anyway? She wasn't exactly overstretched.

As if in answer to my silent ranting, I heard the tap of my mistress's crutches on the stairs above (I had started to call her my mistress as pretending I was Jane Eyre helped me through the day).

Yet now that *Madame* had stirred, no doubt sensing my silent remonstrations, I wished I'd let sleeping dogs lie. Had I tidied the kitchen sufficiently after tea? Were these shoes looking their best despite the damp clods of mud I'd freshly whitened, polish oozing from every crevice?

It took Florence some time to descend the long and winding wooden stairs. I contemplated jumping up to help her, but hoped that if I remained seated she wouldn't notice the enormous splodge of white polish which adorned the step on which I sat.

As she reached the bottom I shuffled to the side to let her pass, the cotton of my dress soaking up the spilt liquid. Florence's hair was half-plaited, half-trailing down her shoulders, static from so many hours in bed. She was still wearing her thin spaghetti-strap top and I considered, not for the first time, the flatness of her bra-less chest. Her nipples were quite prominent. It must take a lot of confidence to thrust them out like that; two cherries on a Mr Kipling's cake.

My employer had changed into yet another pair of bell-bottoms, bright green and red this time. Christmas Pantomime attire. The bottom of one of her plaits was intertwined with three coloured beads – two red and one green – to match her trousers. Looking down at my own outfit I realised that if a stranger knocked at the door, it would be difficult to tell from our clothing who was the employer and who the employee. I would pass as an extra on *Little House on the Prairie* with my long skirts and petticoats, whereas Madame Blanchard leant towards ethnic.

My thoughts were interrupted by the realisation that Florence was sniffing the air. I clicked into focus and observed as she lifted her head up and down like a beagle seeking the scent of a fox, her nostrils flaring as she dragged the air into them with a sudden forced movement.

'*Vous avez déjà préparé le dîner?*' she asked. 'You have already prepared the dinner?"

I felt smug and efficient. There were no flies on me, even if it was my first day.

'*Oui, Florence.* Not only is dinner made, but the children have eaten it. They are in bed.'

Florence looked puzzled and sniffed again.

Maybe she had a cold coming on. Hardly surprising in that skimpy top.

'*Mais je ne sens pas le poulet rôti ?*'

Seeing my puzzled expression, she repeated her question in English, a little more impatiently this time.

'I do not smell roast chicken?'

'No, you smell very nice,' I said. 'Your perfume is lovely.' Although in truth my mistress smelt not so much of perfume as sensible soap. I imagined that all French women bathed in Chanel No. 5. Apparently not. There were other ways in which my mistress had failed to live up to the image I held of a Parisian woman. There was her underwear to start with. It was so utilitarian. It made me ashamed of my own laces and frills. The lacy

99

French boxer shorts from Marks and Sparks. Florence wore those wash and fold knickers you slip into your rucksack when heading off camping: the three-in-a-bag in different colours variety; faded pastels and pinks with grey elastic. *Clearly not making much of an effort for his Lordship*, I'd thought, rolling her knickers into balls down in The Submarine that afternoon. I made a mental note never to let my standards slip once I was married. You could never be too careful. After all, a successful business man, like Axel Blanchard, must be surrounded by girls wearing decent underwear and drenched in perfume. My father's infidelities had left me very wary of the powers of the 'other' woman.

But no matter how sad her knickers were, I could at least reassure Florence, that she did not smell of chicken. '*Tu ne comprends pas*,' she was saying. 'The house, it *should* smell of chicken. It is the children's dinner time soon, and they are having chicken. *Poulet rôti* with salad.

Did you not look in the fridge?'

This was the first I'd heard of chicken. Perhaps Florence didn't know that her mother had brought a bag stuffed full of pastries. The children couldn't possibly have managed a chicken dinner as well.

'Your mother, Bonne-Maman, she came over and we had a big meal,' I said.

Florence's eyes widened. She cast a glance at a thin leather watch on her tiny wrist and frowned, drawing together her thick caterpillar brows.

She turned from me, swinging back into the kitchen. I set down Baptiste's sticky trainer and followed her. She flung open the fridge door. The chicken was on the top shelf wrapped in plastic, like a corpse in a mortician's drawer.

She turned to me with a look of horror.

'But the chicken should not be in *here*, it should be in the oven! The children are going to dine so late. *Ce n'est pas possible!*'

'But they *have* already eaten,' I pleaded. 'They've had their dinner and their bath and now they're ready for bed.' Florence shook her head. 'They will have to have pasta now,' she said. 'It will take too long to roast. You do not understand, it was not their *dinner* that they had with my mother. That was *le goûter*. All French children have it when they come home from school. It is a special treat before homework and dinner.'

'But they ate so much!' I protested. 'Cheese, and bread, and jam, and milk, and yoghurts. When are they meant to fit in dinner?'

'Half past seven, eight o'clock at the latest. And then it is story-time and bed,' Florence said firmly. 'Axel and I dine alone when they are asleep, and the *au pair* is finished. Unless one of us is out. We like our dinner to be animated by adult conversation and not disturbed by *les enfants.*'

Florence had lost patience with me now. She lifted a heavy-based pan, filled it with water, the sinews of her slender arms straining visibly beneath her translucent skin, and slammed it on the gas rink. She opened a packet of pasta and took a sachet of grated cheese from the fridge.

'This must do for tonight,' she said, 'but tomorrow you must be more organised. You must put the chicken in the oven while you are clearing away *le goûter*. All children require a strict timetable if they are to be happy. Everything must happen at the right time, or they will become, how do you say, *énervés*? Fractious.'

My cheeks were burning. I was helpless in this woman's kitchen. She could manage perfectly well without me. I didn't even know *how* to make a roast chicken. Florence looked at her watch again. She unpinned her hair and wiped the back of her neck which exhibited droplets of sweat from so much sudden exertion.

'I must go now,' she said, 'my African drumming night is very important to me. It is such a *release* of all my inner tensions after a busy day. *Vous comprenez*? My friends will be here in a minute. Can you manage?'

'Yes, of course,' I said. 'Drums! How interesting.' Florence smiled and for the first time since our conversation began, looked interested.

'Yes, tonight we are going to La Défense.' 'Isn't that where Monsieur Blanchard works?'

'How clever of you to remember. Yes, Axel works at the top of a skyscraper. His office is in a big building not far from *La Grande Arche*. But I will not see him. My friends *et moi*, we are going down to the metro. We sit on the floor. Well, I can't sit on the floor so well at the moment so I'm taking a stool – and we play the drums. We have had a lot of success with the commuters at rush hour.'

Florence twisted around on her good leg and banged the end of the kitchen table rhythmically, moving up and down as if a whole battery of drums lay at her disposition. She had metamorphosed from strict mother to busker. She stopped and laughed. Her face was flushed and her hair tumbled down her shoulders. I stood, rigid with embarrassment. I'd never managed well in these sorts of circumstances. At school discos, I was always too timid to reach for the ceiling, keeping my own arms clamped firmly by my side as I danced my stiff little crab dance.

'Axel is very embarrassed' she laughed. 'He is such an important man, you know. And there I am! *Me voilà!* Banging the drums as his colleagues board the train home. He does not find it so funny. You may find he is a little bad-tempered tonight. His humour is always black on drum night. And it will be even worse since you have not prepared his chicken.' She sighed; a long-drawn-out sigh of deep fatigue.

'Never mind, he will manage. He will eat bread and cheese.'

CHAPTER 8

Five men with dreadlocks came to collect Florence. She was tiny beside them, frail and sparrow-like. Two of them took her by the arms and bore her away, like an Egyptian princess, a third followed behind carrying her walking sticks. The children rushed down to the doorway to say goodnight, and she kissed each tenderly on the cheek, speaking in low, authoritarian French, stroking cheeks or pinning back a stray lock of hair whilst bestowing that virginal mother and child look she did so well – soulful brown eyes shimmering like velvet moles caught in the moonlight. It occurred to me that the children were saying both hello and goodbye at the same time. By the time Florence returned, which was unlikely to be before midnight, the children would be fast asleep.

Their mother's departure left the children sullen and mutinous. The pasta sat in a bowl in the middle of the kitchen table. There wasn't any sauce, and it had been on the table a while, congealing into a solid mass of intertwined worms. A piece of ham curled on the side of each of our plates.

Delphine delved her spoon in with a squelching sound like wellies in mud. Her face was strained, her expression one I'd taken pains to study in the drama studio at school: traces of horror etched onto its sharp little features. Her spoon hovered an instant and then with a flick of the wrist she slopped the pasta back into the bowl. Her French was a rapid quick fire, and I understood none of it.

'Berk, c'est dégueulasse. Elle veut nous empoisonner avec des vers mouilleés.'

I caught the word *empoisonner*. It was close enough to English to work out. Later I translated the full sentence with my Collin's Dictionary.

Yuck, it's disgusting. She's trying to poison us with wet worms!

I was about to protest when Delphine returned to the bowl a second time. I was hopeful she'd decided to give it a go, but she lifted the spoon high above her head and flicked it hard into the air, sending a Scud missile of pasta across the kitchen to land against the door of the fridge. Baptiste and Clémence shrieked in joy, grabbing their spoons with fervour and following suit. Baptiste fired his spoonful against the window, while Clémence stood up on her chair and aimed for the ceiling light.

By this point the three children were out of control. Pasta worms were strung from the ceiling and walls like Christmas garlands, or sliding their weary way down the oven door.

There was a lot I wanted to say in French, but I didn't have the words.

'*Arrêtez!*' was all I could come up with. '*Arrêtez ça tout de suite.*'

Baptiste decided not only to ignore my pleas, but to take things to the next level. His spoon lost on the floor now, he delved his hand into the bowl, scooping out the pasta and squeezing great clumps until the butter ran down his fingers. He slammed his load hard onto the crown of Clémence's head, who screamed, jumping to her feet and kicking over the stool. All hell had broken loose when the shrill ring of the doorbell cut through the mayhem. We froze, just as if we were playing musical statues, Delphine poised to whack a fist full of pasta into Baptiste's face. Please god don't let it be that bossy grandmother again. Or Axel Blanchard who had forgotten his key.

I unhooked a worm from my cleavage and exited the kitchen. There was a shadow at the glass. I pulled open the heavy old door, stunned to find Jessica my friend from school; my sixth-form classmate who I also knew to be au-pairing somewhere in the city. She must have phoned home and asked dad for my address. There was a large suitcase at her feet.

'Well, aren't you going to invite a girl in?' she asked, and pushed forward, dumping her case in the hallway. She sauntered in and looked around with a satisfied air.

'Not bad,' she said. 'You've landed on your feet. Family in?'

'No, the father is still at work, and the mother's gone …

drumming … in the metro.'

Jessica shrugged as if this was normal. Her eyes narrowed as she spied three dishevelled children lined up by the kitchen door. More like Fagin's urchins than the Von Trapp children now. She looked at me, then back at the children.

'*Mais alors*' she said, in a voice reminiscent of our old headmaster when he walked into a classroom of disarray. '*Mais qu'est-ce que c'est tout ça?*'

Delphine looked sheepish and grabbed her sister's hand. Clémence started to cry. Jessica was having none of it. She was Julie Andrews. All those boxing-days spent watching *The Sound of Music* had stood her in good stead.

She slipped off her coat to reveal a black pinafore dress, with a white blouse and black stockings. Her shoes were as sensible as a traffic warden's. Three years ago, she'd worn vintage clothes from Oxfam, specialising in silk flapper dresses as we lounged on the back lawn of her Victorian semi on a grotty council estate, playing at *Brideshead Revisited*. The ITV version. Her hair was dyed black back then and cut in a bob the shape of a pudding bowl, white foundation caked on her face like a 1920s consumptive; a protest at the Duran Duran mania sweeping across our school.

Today she was dressed for another part: the English nanny.

She caught my surprised glance. 'Oh, this?' she said, flicking at her full skirts. 'You've got to look the part, *n'est ce pas?* – or the little brats won't take you seriously.'

With her hands on her hips Jessica ordered the children to tidy away their plates and unhook pasta worms from wherever they were hanging. They obeyed in silence while she watched their every move, her crimson lips pursed in displeasure.

Before long the battlefield was clear. The children hadn't eaten a thing, but two hours earlier they'd stuffed their faces with enough cheese and bread to feed a small French village. They wouldn't starve. Not by English standards.

Half an hour later the children had been scrubbed within an inch of their lives and were in bed. It was their second bath of the day, but this one had taken place under the stern command of Jessica, who handed Baptiste his own 'glove' and told him to stop being such a baby and to wash his own arse. They didn't really need a second bath, but Jessica said it would calm them.

Even Delphine obeyed without a squeak. If anything, the elder girl had shown nothing but respect for my friend's military organisation, borne not so much from a love of discipline, as a desire to *get the little bastards in bed so we can have a drink*.

It was the first time I had experienced this French love of authority, and it would not be the last. The nicer you were, the harder it was. Results could only be achieved with the demonstration of an iron will. It was the zero tolerance approach to mothering, and it applied not just to childcare, but to every aspect of French life. If you say please and thank you too many times in a French restaurant it is a well-known fact that, at best, the service will be terrible, at worse, they will spit in your food. 'How the English grovel' my French husband would tell me some years later, 'how many times must *les anglais* thank the waiter. What they do not understand is that he is there to serve, and all these pleases and thank yous show nothing but weakness, and are a reminder to him of his servility. Say it once like you mean it, with guts, and only then will you be shown respect, given the table you want, or have your food served on time.' The French respected authority and people who instilled the fear of god in them. Later I would learn that the whole educational system was built on this premise. If a child scored nineteen out of twenty in a test, the teacher did not praise the nineteen but beat the stuffing out of it for losing a point.

Love of discipline was genetic, and it was immediately clear that Delphine, Clémence and Baptiste had far more respect for Jessica than they would ever have for me. They wanted her to smile and to like them because she did not. It was the equivalent of chasing after lovers who couldn't commit. The children sensed that I was seeking their approval and my weakness was repulsive to them.

Delphine was the first to ask my friend to tuck her up in bed. She allowed Jessica to smooth down her sheets, and to give her a cold peck on the cheek before switching off her light. Clémence trotted at her heels like a lamb, until finally Jessica, tiring of her new-found shadow, scooped her up and plonked her down onto her tiny bed. Baptiste put himself to bed with a comic book and a promise to Jessica that he would read only five minutes longer.

I knew he would not disobey.

The children had been quiet for over half an hour. Jessica had found the drinks cabinet in the salon and poured us both a full glass of port, topping the bottle back up with water.

'Drink it fast,' she said, 'they might be back soon.'

We knocked it back and she poured a second glass. I felt nauseous with stress and fatigue but the alcohol blurred the edges and I began to relax. Being on my best behaviour in another woman's home was exhausting. We rinsed the glasses, put them back exactly where we'd found them and returned to the kitchen table.

'Any food?' she asked.

I told her about the chicken, and how worried I was about having to make it the next day. She laughed and rolled up her Julie Andrew sleeves.

'Let's do it now' she said. 'That way I can teach you how and we can have a bit for dinner.'

She slammed the chicken onto a chopping board while I hunted out some sea salt, an onion and a bottle of olive oil, as instructed.

'First, we peel the onion,' she said. 'Second, we stick it up its arse, first checking the butcher has taken out the organs. Here they are. Dump those, will you. See? Easy. Seen my mother do it loads of times.'

She lifted a flap of dead skin and inserted the onion.

Then with a dash of sea salt, a sprinkling of herbs and a lug of unctuous golden olive oil, she rubbed the chicken up and down in a non-committal fashion, squeezing the skin with her deft fingers, lifting the carcass up by its legs so that she could do both sides.

She stuck it in the oven and while we were waiting for it to cook, she filled me in on what had been happening in her life. I told her about David.

'So, he's said the relationship is over, right?'

'Right.'

'And he hasn't written to you in three weeks?"

'No.'

'And he told you quite categorically *not* to come to Paris?'

'Yep.'

She stared at me with a look of exasperation and shook her head.

'What about you?' I asked, wanting to change the subject. 'How are you getting on with your family? Night off tonight is it?"

She took a moment to reply, then smiled.

'Fired,' she said, 'From my third family. I'll have to go back to the agency at some point. I'll stay with you till then'

'Stay here? But I don't know if they'll mind. Fired what for?'

'Boiled eggs.' 'What?'

'Boiled eggs. I gave the kids boiled eggs every night for two weeks.'

'Why?'

She shrugged. 'Saves time. I wanted to go into Paris, and they only take three and a half minutes. Four at a push. If you tear off a bit of the egg carton, it makes a perfect cup; saves on the washing up.'

She pulled her sleeves back down, and carefully buttoned the grubby looking cuffs of her blouse, covering her white and slightly podgy arms. Despite her outwardly slender appearance, Jessica hated sport and had the soft flabby skin of someone who preferred life indoors, curled up on a couch with a book. I remembered how the summer sun would burn her when we were out on cross-country – puffing along at the back, wanting to slip off into the woods for a fag. Her hair was naturally a pale ginger but was hennaed deepest red these days. It suited her better than the severe black of our school years. She had always cut it herself, with varying degrees of success. Today she had a ruler-straight fringe half an inch above her eyebrows, and a square bob cropped into the back of her neck, the quirky shade of red a note of folly in an otherwise perfect impersonation of a Victorian nanny.

'It was all fine to begin with,' she said, 'I mean the baby, he's only two ... well, he didn't complain. He *liked* having toasted soldiers every night. But the girl, Juliette, she's five, started to complain that she was suffering from *des gazes* – you know, farting. Sulphur farts. Her mother had the nerve to go through a week of bins to find out what I'd been feeding them. She found twenty-one egg boxes.'

'So, they chucked you out? The parents?'

'There was only the mother. The husband had run off with his marketing assistant. A tall blonde named Laetitia. He didn't leave them with much money. The mother was never there: out all day at the office and she expected me to do the shopping on a pittance. Even if I'd wanted to, I wouldn't have been able to buy much. Not meat or fish for sure!'

The aroma of chicken filled the kitchen. Jessica sourced a jar of peas and some instant mash at the back of the kitchen cupboard. Its sell-by date was two years past, but we were too hungry too care. Anyway, I was on safe territory with instant mash. We served up, slicing the chicken carefully so that it wouldn't look as if we'd taken too much; a fine slither from under the wings, a strip or two from the bottom of the legs.

I'd just popped the first delicious forkful into my mouth when the front door slammed and I heard footsteps in the hallway. I jumped to attention nearly choking. Jessica remained seated, head tilted back with a snotty look, as if entertaining in her own kitchen.

In walked Monsieur Blanchard, wrestling with his tie. He stared at the two of us, and from his puzzled glance I could see he couldn't remember which of us he had employed. He'd barely glanced at me in the car.

'*Florence est là?*' he asked, hedging his bets and addressing the space between us.

'*Non. Elle n'est pas là.* She's still out.' I was careful not to mention the word 'drums.' I didn't want to set him off.

Jessica stood up, smiling sweetly, and extended her hand. '*Je suis Jessica, enchantée.*'

She pointed to the empty chair beside her and pulled it out, saying something in French which must have been the equivalent of 'Hard day at the office, darling?' Monsieur Blanchard sat down heavily, his face etched with fatigue. Jessica fetched him a plate. If anything, he looked grateful to be taken care of. She took the blue silk tie from his hand and folded it carefully, wrapping it softly around her own. I set a plate for him and he started to eat at once, staring at his food with the vacant look of a man who had given his all in the last twelve hours. He asked Jessica if she might be so kind as to pass him the red wine. I noticed he didn't ask me. He poured a glass from the half bottle left over from Hugo and Marcel's lunchtime feast. Seeing that Jessica had taken the initiative to bring over three glasses he poured the last of it out for us. The wine's heady aroma filled the air with a whiff of wealth.

I was too tired, and too tipsy after the port, to attempt to speak French. Revived by this stage, and appearing to remember who I was, Monsieur Blanchard shot me a direct look.

'Have you been into Paris yet?'

'No,' I replied, and then, emboldened by the wine, and touched that he had thought to ask, I added: 'You see, I don't have any money yet.'

'Ah,' he replied thoughtfully, swirling the wine in his glass. '*Je vois*. I see.'

I hoped he might stick his hands into his back pocket, but he stared thoughtfully into his glass, and I could tell he was no longer thinking about me or my lack of wages. Jessica said something I didn't quite catch, and he grinned, his lips parting to reveal what I'd often heard my mother call 'a good set of teeth'. I didn't know what Jessica had said, but for a second he looked less of a man in a grey suit, less of a managing director of very important matters, and more like the young boy he must once have been.

The kitchen was in disarray once more. Life had become a constant round of kitchen cleaning. How many meals was it possible to fit into one day? I left the table and started to tidy up. Jessica did not offer to help, but remained at the table, her head resting on her hands, leaning forwards to catch Monsieur Blanchard's every word. The conversation grew animated. From what I could understand, above the sound of running water, a transaction was taking place between them.

'Deal!' said Monsieur Blanchard, the English catching my attention. He swigged the last of the wine and banged his glass on the table.

'Deal!' said Jessica, banging her glass down too. She reached across the table and they clasped hands.

Jessica glanced over to the sink where I was busy scrubbing pans. 'I'm moving into the cottage and helping out with the gardening until Florence is better,' she announced. 'I might be doing a bit of painting, too.'

The cottage, I discovered, was a house at the bottom of the garden. The first I'd heard of any such place. I was soon to discover that this was a small stone building, in a row of neat, white houses in the street behind which led to the station. It was not a grand turn-of-the-century house like the main house, but it served its purpose. Monsieur Blanchard explained that when he and his wife heard it had come onto the market, they decided it would be silly not to buy it, as the two gardens backed onto one another and it effectively removed any issue of vis-à-vis with the neighbours: a sizeable chunk of money to pay for peace and quiet. The main door was in the street on the other side, a short walk around the block. The easiest and most direct way into to the cottage was across the lawn from the terrace at the back of the house. As we crossed the gardens I felt a rising sense of curiosity and adventure.

Monsieur Blanchard led the way, shining his torch across the lawn, and through the overgrown brambles at the bottom of the garden, as we followed behind. We were all wearing rubber boots, fished out from the top of the cellar stairs. The evening had taken on a *Famous Five* feel by now. Even Monsieur Blanchard had adopted a spirit of adventure. He fiddled with the door key until it finally opened, flicked on a switch in the electric box and illuminated the building.

The room was spacious with a patchy undercoat of white paint. The internal walls had been removed, so that there was no longer a separate hallway, kitchen, or sitting room. Lines across the floor traced a pathway across the black-and-white turn-of-the-century floor tiles, where once there had been partitions.

The furniture was plain and simple. A white armchair, a scrubbed pine table, a set of bookshelves and a bed in the corner made up with white sheets, four big fluffy pillows, and a raspberry throw.

'We wanted the feel of a loft,' Monsieur Blanchard said. 'Florence wanted to house political refugees here. I thought it better to stick the *au pair* here, to give us some privacy.' (I prickled at the implication that I would *want* to get in their way!) 'And finally, since we could not agree, the house sits empty. Jessica may use it, in return for the jobs she has promised she will do.'

'Jobs?' I asked.

Jessica waved her hand vaguely, 'Oh, giving this place a fresh coat of paint, a little light gardening, helping you in the house if you need me', and then in a much lower voice, so only I could hear, 'not that I'll have an overabundance of spare time for you, what with my novel writing and all.'

CHAPTER 9

I was back in The Submarine ironing, Jenny Murray crackling away on *Woman's Hour*. I was feeling tearful. David hadn't written a single letter. Surely if he had, Rafi would have forwarded it on. Not only this but it was day two, and I hadn't been into Paris yet. There had been no mention of money, or payment, and I wondered if I was expected to wait until the end of the month.

Jessica, meanwhile, had settled in like a pig in muck. Florence merely smiled when Axel told her over breakfast that morning that he had effectively complied with her wishes and housed a refugee. Florence, showing immediate concern for the well-being of said refugee, ordered me down to the cottage with a basket of freshly washed towels, in case 'the poor girl' (*la pauvre*) had been ejected from her previous family without any, arming me with a bag of goodies, including tea and coffee, milk, bread and jam. There was no mention as to *why* Jessica was homeless, or any reference made to the fact that the situation was of her own making. Carrying a wicker basket of victuals across the lawn that morning like Little Red Riding Hood, I was struck by the beauty of the cottage in the early morning sunshine.

There was a small gateway hewn into the Blanchard's main garden wall, carving a narrow passageway through the stone. The wall was covered in flouncy pink roses like the *Secret Garden* and so well camouflaged I hadn't noticed it. The robin was back, tame as anything, bobbing across the soft mossy lawn, taking flight to the nearest branch as it saw me. Two blackbirds chirruped cheerfully from a tree above, reminding me that bird song was the same the world over. It was an unexpectedly bucolic scene, so close to Paris.

Jessica was stirring, bleary-eyed, beneath the crisp white linen sheets. Her mascara lay in streaks beneath her eyes and on the pillow. The strict black nanny's dress she had worn hung over the back of the chair like an afterthought. Propping herself up on her pillows, like a convalescent in a nursing home, she grabbed my wicker basket, examining the contents hungrily.

It occurred to me that Jessica had the better deal. Whereas my room was adjacent to the children's, and within a floor's reach of the Blanchards themselves should they need me, Jessica had a whole cottage to herself, so far from their daily needs she wouldn't have heard them if they'd been murdered in their beds. My friend's new home was equipped with a kettle, a fridge and a coffee machine. She had acquired total independence on the back of being my friend. This would have been a perfect place for David and me to hang out at the weekends.

'What did he say you have to do exactly?' I asked.

'Not much. Paint this place, when I feel up to it, and help with the garden.'

'When you feel up to it? You've not been ill! You've been fired! Is that it?'

'Yup!' she said, stretching out lazily beneath the quilt, 'I think he quite likes me. He had a twinkle in his eye. A certain *je ne sais quoi*. I think I'll do very well in the house of Axel Blanchard.'

I'd been up since seven o'clock and had already over-seen the children's breakfast *and* re-ironed Axel's work shirt, which I'd discovered hanging ominously on my bedroom door-handle in silent protest at the standard of my work. Admittedly the collar was a bit scrunched, and I'd pressed the iron into the wrong fold and com-pletely forgotten the cuffs. I sneaked back down to The Submarine in shame, correcting my mistakes, hanging the now twice-ironed shirt back onto the Master's own bedroom door handle. This done, I woke the children and gave them breakfast: cereal, with a dozen boxes all spread out over the table as they liked to mix up concoc-tions in their bowls. After this I walked them to school, came home to tidy the kitchen and, at the request of Fuschia, carried a breakfast tray laden with tea and goodies to Florence's room.

These tasks had been completed before Jessica had opened a sleepy eye. I thought back to my friend's lazy breakfast in bed, as I slammed the iron down hard on Axel's cuffs and collars. I didn't think I could bear the humiliation of finding another shirt hanging on my door handle in the morning. I hung the finished piece, a striped blue and white number, with an all-white collar, reminiscent of the sort of shirts men in Wall Street wear and considered it with the same pride I had once reserved for a perfectly balanced essay on the metaphysical poets. It was amazing how utterly useless my education felt in my new role as a washerwoman. Were there any famous washerwomen in any of the books I had read? The only image which came to mind was Toad disguised in washerwoman clothes when he escaped from prison in *The Wind in the Willows*. In contrast, Jessica was a gardener, and gardeners held a far more prominent place in literature. There was D.H. Lawrence for a start, with the gardener stealing the heart of Lady Chatterley and getting up to all sorts in the process.

Being 'in service' took some getting used to, after the high hopes of university and long before the advent of *Downton Abbey*. There was a readjustment to be made. My grandmother had gone to work as a maid in a big Edwardian home at the age of fourteen. There was a picture of her pinning sheets onto a washing line wearing a mop cap and frilly apron. I felt a pang of sorrow. I'd not seen Gran for a while. She'd been unwell and the last time I was home, my parents had argued and refused to drive me there. All too soon the holidays were over and I had left without seeing her. I felt the usual sense of stomach-wrenching anguish at the thought of losing her. She had given me all the love my own mother never could.

The laundry basket beside me was still full. I reached for a pair of crumpled jeans – Axel's, judging by the length of the legs. I flattened them out onto the ironing board and began my work, blinking back the tears. What was I doing here? I should be at home taking care of my grandmother. I'd promised her when I was a little girl: *I'll always look after you when you are old. You'll never be alone or go into a home.*

There was a lump in the pocket. The lining must have doubled up inside. Surprised, I pull out a crumpled note – 500 French francs. I flattened it and applied the iron gently to the surface, the faces of Pierre and Marie Curie staring back at me in green print. It was the equivalent of fifty pounds, or thereabouts; more than enough to buy a ticket into Paris.

Jessica had explained that morning that I needed a *carte orange,* a monthly train pass that allowed unlimited transport in and out of the city, on any train, day or night. I needed to have my photograph taken in one of the booths at Monoprix, the local supermarket. The *carte orange* was quite costly but an absolute necessity. It wasn't as if the family had bothered to ask if I needed an advance! I'd been working non-stop, with no mention of any time off. Anyway, what kind of man left 500 francs in his pocket without noticing it was gone? *The kind of man who buys a house just to make sure no-one else can,* replied my inner devil. Perhaps I could borrow it for a few days and then put it back when they paid me. I could go into Paris, search for David and find out if there was any point staying here in this ridiculous job. If there wasn't I might as well go back home. Wherever that was. No-one would know if I took this forgotten note. I folded it neatly in my pocket. As I came up the stairs carrying a big basket of ironed clothes, I met Florence. She was leaning on one crutch in the hallway, the morning mail in her hand. I put the basket down and fished the 500-franc note from my pocket. I couldn't do it. Even borrowing it for a short time felt wrong. I'd never stolen anything in my life. I'd just have to stay indoors until they decided to pay me.

'I found this,' I said, 'in the pocket of the trousers of Monsieur Blanchard.' It was funny when I spoke English to the French, how I twisted the words of my sentences around so they made sense.

Florence took the note and smiled. She slipped it into her pocket without a word and carried on down the hallway calling to me to bring her coffee in the salon.

That night, after *le goûter*, Clémence came to me all smiles and kisses. Delphine watched disapprovingly. Clémence said something in rapid French so I threw Delphine a questioning glance. It was exhausting not understanding what was being said, and I found that as the day progressed, my head hurt more and more from straining to comprehend.

'She says you can stay,' said Delphine with a shrug.

'You passed the test.'

I didn't understand. Clémence said something else and pulled me by the hand, dragging me up the stairs to her mother's wing of the house. I stopped at the door. I didn't want to go in. Florence might be in bed. I hadn't been to this part of the house before, and even the children were not welcome here.

Clémence tugged at my hand, *'Viens,'* she said. *'Maman veut te voir.'*

I allowed her to pull me inside. The first room, which was a library, served as an antechamber. Bookshelves lined the walls, laden with the kind of thick, heavily bound editions which collected dust and which no-one ever seemed to read. There was a wooden ladder propped against the shelf, hooked to a rail which ran the length of the room. The room had two comfortable winged-back armchairs, and an oriental rug thrown over the parquet floor in red, pink and gold. A large ornate desk sat in the middle of the room. I didn't know enough about antiques to know from which period it originated, but it had a leather top with gold edges, gently bowed legs and tiny golden tips at its feet like dainty slippers.

Florence was sitting at the desk, her crutches flayed out beside her. Her hair was scraped back in a sensible knot, and she had removed her African beads. Her face was pale, and she had the weary look of someone who had been mining coal all day. She smiled weakly and opened a golden drawer before her. The drawer was heavy and she tugged it, using both hands. She beckoned me to her side. Inside the drawer was a row of wooden slats: fifty or more perhaps. Between each of the wooden slats lay a bundle of notes. Many were the colour of the 500-franc note retrieved from Axel's jeans, others so high in value I didn't recognise them. I'd never seen so much money. Not even at Barclay's. There must have been 100,000 francs at least – more perhaps. It was like Monopoly money, stashed in its box at the end of the game. Florence plucked two green notes from a middle section and handed them to me. Their absence in the compartment barely left a dent.

'This is for now,' she said, 'You must make it last for a couple of weeks. I will give you more at the end of the month. By then we will both know if we are happy with each other, *n'est-ce pas?*'

She closed the drawer, retrieved her sticks, and hobbled into the bedroom. Down a corridor I glimpsed the open door of a bathroom, and beyond it the bedroom with a large, comfortable-looking bed, piled high with white pillows. Florence turned and gave a sharp nod. This was my signal to leave. With the children's *goûter* sitting heavy in their stomachs, I now needed to think about dinner.

I set about peeling some carrots and potatoes. Delphine remained at the kitchen table. There wasn't any reason for her to be there, but she watched me impassively. I remembered her earlier comment about my having passed some sort of test and decided to ask her.

She smiled. 'In Papa's trousers, the ones you washed, there was some money,' she said. 'My parents always play this trick when there is a new girl. To see if you take the money – to see if you are honest.'

I flushed red, even though I knew I'd passed the test. Thank god I didn't do anything stupid.

'But what if I hadn't seen it?' I said, 'I might not have.'

'Then it would still be there,' she said, 'and you would not be ironing the trousers correctly. Either you are a thief or you are no good at your job.' 'Have some girls failed the test?' 'Failed?'

'Yes, you know – not passed; taken the money.'

'Of course,' she laughed. 'Papa drives those girls away the very same day.'

Straight to prison. Do not pass 'Go'.

I could see I was going to have to watch my step in the house of Axel Blanchard.

CHAPTER 10

It was Saturday lunchtime, the start of my weekend. My time off! I was going to see David. I wouldn't phone beforehand. I'd go there and catch him by surprise. If I called, he might tell me not to come. I was going to find his apartment, and knock on the door. If he wasn't in, I'd find out when he'd be back. I opened my Collin's pocket dictionary and wrote out exactly what I wanted to say, allowing for all possible outcomes.

I called into the garden cottage on my way out. Jessica had only just got up. She was sitting drinking coffee in an armchair, folded up in a long white nightdress, reading a crumpled Penguin edition of *Madame Bovary*. I noticed that there was much scoring and underlining of favourite passages, and notes written in the margin in her cramped and spidery handwriting. She said she was going to potter in the garden and prune the roses, so she wouldn't come to the station with me. But she told me what to do and where to go. There was a Monoprix on my way. I needed to go in there, get my photo taken, and then go to the RER fast-train station, which was about a fifteen-minute walk. At the *guichet* I needed to ask for *'une carte orange, trois zones, s'il vous plaît.'* I was living outside Paris so it was important I got a three-zone ticket in order to get home safely again.

This was my first big adventure into the city alone, and I was keenly wired. I'd washed my hair. It'd grown past my shoulders and was blonde from the summer sun. I clipped up the middle section and brushed down the sides. This made me look too young and schoolgirlish, so when I got to Monoprix, I bought some bright red lipstick and blusher. I always felt better equipped to face the world with my blusher in place.

I found a photo booth and used the mirror inside to make myself up. The girl at the till had given me some loose change, so the whole process was simple enough. When I look at the pictures today I see a startled looking girl with eyes full of hope, and very red lips and cheeks. As I pulled the still warm picture into my hand that day, I wondered how I would feel by sunset. Would it be a day of joy or sadness? I wondered if David would take me in his arms and kiss me passionately, happy that I had followed him to France. What greater proof of love could I have given?

I was wearing my long baggy tent dress from Aberystwyth, and flat shoes for walking. As I passed the French women in the street I felt decidedly *English*. French women had that neat way of dressing which was beyond me: tight little jeans and jackets nipped in at the waist, with a silk scarf slotted in the collar. Students my age wore ubiquitous long scarves which they wrapped around their necks several times, as if to hold their heads on – not just the girls, but the boys too. I found myself staring at the men more than the women. The aesthetically knotted white scarves reminded me of Lawrence of Arabia. Or Yasser Arafat. Some men carried neat black leather bags, with long shoulder straps which were quite *girlie*. David had a bag like this. He wore it over his shoulders and kept his purse and comb inside. I couldn't imagine the Ifor Evans rugby lot carrying *handbags*. The lads stuffed fivers into the back pockets of their jeans and kept loose change at the front, consciously padding out their tackle. David had a neat little leather wallet for bank notes and a special squishy leather purse, like a small sausage with a zip down the middle, in which he kept his loose change. Like most Frenchmen, he didn't drink to *get smashed* but sipped wine with his meals. He didn't qualify a good night out by the number of times he'd vomited, whereas my old rugby chums would knock back ten pints, heave the last two up on the beach and then head back for more – a bulimic manner of drinking punctuated by a traditional feast of chips and curry sauce between rounds to line the stomach for more.

My French lover had taught me that it was okay to carry a girlie bag and keep your money in a sausage purse if you were comfortable with your sexuality. It was also okay for a man to wear a silk scarf or a pink shirt, and sip wine from a delicate glass.

David was perfect – and my life would be too. Once I'd tracked him down.

I had imagined that the train line would be something like the metro I'd taken in the city with David earlier that year; an underground line running all the way to central Paris. However, I found myself up above ground, by a golden coloured station, from which the SNCF Paris Saint Lazare line ran. I bought my *carte orange* from the *guichet*, amputating a massive chunk from my wages, then stepped out onto a concrete platform to wait for the train.

The sun was shining but there were only a few stray travellers about. The train wasn't due for fifteen minutes. I sat on a plastic bench and filled in my name and address on the *carte orange*. I was properly Parisian now. This finished, there wasn't much else to do, and I'd forgotten my book. Glancing towards the platform opposite I whimpered, momentarily confused. Staring across at me, with familiar piercing blue eyes, and clad in that pin-striped suit I knew so well, was a giant-sized Axel Blanchard.

I tiptoed to the edge of the platform for a better view. The billboard displayed three men on the front of an advert for a business magazine. Axel, centre forward, was in the most important position of the three, pushing his way forward against a dramatic black backdrop in one of those 'breaking barriers' postures. His silver-blonde hair was neatly clipped, his lips parted over those 'well-attended to by dentists in early childhood' teeth. He was *massive* – literally. Like Gulliver in the land of the Lilliputians.

My employer made front page news. People paid good money to read of his exploits in glossy print. Axel edged to the front of the poster as I stared, or so it appeared, the letters above his head announcing: 'LES NOUVEAUX ENTREPRENEURS'.

There he was. My new boss. Making inroads into French history.

I realised that a row of Axel Blanchards lined the platform wall. Turning to look behind me, I saw that there was yet another poster behind me. A paper-thin Axel Blanchard loomed over me like an avenging angel, brandishing a crumpled shirt. The train pulled in, I stepped on board and the doors buzzed quickly closed. As we gathered speed through the dreary suburbs into Paris, I watched Axel Blanchard posters flash before my eyes. The man I worked for was important enough to have wall-papered every station we passed – the same man who entrusted me with the care of his jaunty underwear, and his children.

I sat down on the blue and red train seat. The air was warm, and the window half down. As the train gathered speed, pulling me away from my life as a *jeune fille au pair*, I heaved a sigh of relief. I felt free for the first time in days. I didn't have to cook, or wash or iron.

I was on my way to Paris!

My heart soared as high as a Paris pigeon, and I watched in amusement as a young guy with a baseball cap danced in the doorway to the train, the wires of his Walkman dangling from his ears. This was the kind of place Paris was. You could boogie in trains and no-one cared.

Even Florence could play her drums on the station platform, the poster of her husband looming large above her head. The song which consumed the guy in front of me must have had an intense beat. Rap maybe. He was in the zone now, oblivious to his surroundings, moving rhythmically and swaying as the train screeched precariously around bends. There was no-one else in the carriage. It was lunchtime and most French people were still *à table*.

My eyes wandered up and down, taking in the man's baggy sports jacket and oversized trainers. Sensing my eyes upon him, he turned half a degree. No more. This was all it took. From where I was sitting I had a front-row view. The man wasn't dancing, he was masturbating. He must have been timing his journey in accordance with his needs, for as the train pulled into the station, his solitary dance came to a zealous end. He zipped his jeans back up, jumped down and sailed off jauntily down the platform. I descended as quickly as I could, stepping onto the platform, beneath the impressive vaulted iron ceiling, descending directly into a life-size version of Claude Monet's rendering of La Gare Saint Lazare. There was no hiss of steam, no clouds of smoke, but otherwise it was still the same.

I was in a painting. I was in Paris! This was why I had come here. Anything was possible. It was magical. There was the metro line to Montmartre or to the Champs Elysées. I could sit at the Deux-Magots café and read a book, like Sartre or de Beauvoir. Or pop into Shakespeare and Company as Hemmingway had so often done, when cadging the loan of a free book from Sylvia Beach.

I could do all these things and more, but first I needed to find David.

It took me over an hour to decipher the map and after several stops and changes, to exit at the right station. I had walked these streets before, on a spring day earlier that year, though of course my visit had remained a state secret. Retracing our steps, I realised how close we were to David's family home. It was as if he had wanted to show me everything he could, without crossing that final threshold. He'd been playing with fire, knowing we might bump into his parents, his brother or one of his many cousins, at any time. Had he wanted to be discovered, like the lover who allowed his mistress to press her lipstick to his collar?

I was at the junction between the rue des Rosiers and the rue Ferdinand-Duval. There was the Jo Goldenberg Deli on the corner where we'd eaten a few months earlier.

I paused for a moment in the doorway and remembered how David had told me of the terrible terrorist attack that had taken place here. Gunmen had fired into the busy restaurant one lunchtime claiming the lives of six customers and injuring many others. A direct attack against the Jewish community of Paris. The restaurant was teeming as it had been on our first visit. I knew David's address by heart, but now that I was here in the rue des Rosiers, I fumbled for the paper in my pocket to allow myself a few minutes of grace. My heart was pounding and I felt sick. Walking on, I arrived at the door of his apartment much faster than I would have liked. I realised that I couldn't get in unless I knew the digicode and, of course, David had not felt the need to share this.

I stood before the monumentally ornate door and waited. There was a café across the road. I could sit there until I saw him and buy myself a drink. More money wasted. I was contemplating my next move, when the door opened and a man with long black ringlets and a kippah came out. He brushed past me without a word, but I managed to catch the door before it closed and slipped inside.

I found myself in a covered entrance hall, which was cobbled and smelt of bleach, the floor still damp where it had just been cleaned. There was a row of letter boxes and I searched for David's name. Nothing. I checked again. There was no-one with this name. There were two staircases, one to my left and one to my right. The steps on each side of the hallway were covered with a plush red carpet, pinned back with golden bars. There were two lifts in black wrought iron: open-cast affairs, their perilous-looking cords hanging down the lift shaft. I was debating which staircase to choose, planning to knock on every door if I must, when a woman came out of an entrance by the bins, wearing a headscarf and a blue apron, and carrying a broom. She saw me and smiled.

'*Bonjour madame. Je peux vous aider?*'

I showed her the name and the address on my paper. She tutted and shook her head. '*Il est parti*,' she said, and to make sure I had fully understood, she flapped her hand towards the door: 'Gone, gone!'

'*Où est-il parti?*' I asked, in my best textbook French.

Where has he gone? '*La Réunion.*'

I shook my head. The name meant nothing to me. It must be another district of Paris.

'*Il y a un metro?*' I asked. The woman laughed and shook her head. She took my arm and asked me to wait a minute. I remained in the hallway, wondering if she had gone to fetch someone who could speak English. She was back a moment later with a young boy – probably her son. He was carrying an atlas. The two of them consulted the index, with much contradiction and page-flicking, pulling the book this way and that, before they finally held open a page and the woman jabbed a disinfectant-smelling finger at a spot in the middle.

'*C'est là, madame. Voilà! Regardez.*'

I looked at the place where she was pointing. It wasn't in Paris.

It wasn't even in France.

It was an island in the Indian Ocean.

David had gone, but when I returned home, dusty and defeated, there was news of him. Jessica was waiting with a blue airmail envelope, as thin as the tissue into which I was about to sob. There was much crossing out on the front cover. It had been sent first to Aberystwyth, then redirected to Paris in Rafi's square and ruler-straight print.

Jessica was sitting in a garden chair reading, wearing a big straw hat and sunglasses. The last rays of sunlight were falling, the petals from the roses she'd snipped lay sprinkled like confetti around her feet, the branches above her head chopped haphazardly.

'I steamed it open,' she said. 'It's bad.'

Judging by the crumples along the seal, I could see that she had read it, then stuck it back down, but I was too desperate to read it to care. David's loopy handwritten words were as flowery as the rose-garden in which we sat, each word penetrating my heart like a fist of thorns.

My dearest one,

Forgive my silence, I have been at war with myself and with my thoughts.

It is ordained in France, by those bastards in Government, these (excuse my French) 'salauds', that each male over the age of eighteen must do one year of military service. Twelve months of our lives wasted forever. The only way out is to feign madness, but the only madness of which I can speak is my last few crazy months with you. When I learnt I was to be sent far away, I admit the coward in me did not say no. I thought the distance between us might help us both in our suffering.

Now my hair (as you would say) is 'short, back and sides' and my face so brown with the sun that you would not recognise your poor David.

Yet, if I am to be a soldier, I tell you that my only battle is to heal the bruises I have made in your heart. Peace will only come for me when I know you are happy and have moved on, for I should have been strong and resisted your charms. I should never have allowed our love to be.

I am what Rafi calls 'a complete bastard'.

Here on my island, the skies are hot and burning blue, the sand is golden, and the Pacific ocean is flat as the turquoise plate on which Rafi served our chapati. It is not like the sea that roared to our grief by the fish and chip shop, at the end of the pier in Aberystwyth. Yet in my thoughts, I am not here by these still waters. My heart is with you in Dyfed, where the rain could always hide our tears. I must be brave, and so must you.

I imagine, and hope, that you have followed your heart's desire and found a job with your much-loved Royal Shakespeare Company. Perhaps one day I will see you on stage, and sit and cheer with my children. We will not understand a word you say, but we will know you are the best of all the Shakespearian actresses in England.

You will find this hard to read, but believe me when I say, I know I loved you, for it has taken me many months to enjoy the making of love to other women. This is how I know, that you, my dearest Kiki, were different from all the rest.

Be happy in this life.

If ever you need a friend, I will always be, Your ever loving, David

'He's shagging other women,' Jessica said.

I ran from the garden to the house, wanting to be alone, wanting to sob my heart out until the pain stopped. The bastard had dared to admit that he was finally enjoying making love to another woman! And in the prelude to this final enjoyment, there were *other* times when he'd been making love to women *without* enjoying it – but doing his best all the same! Was that meant to be a compliment? Were French men so stupid? An English man might have cheated, but to *write* it as though he'd finally made progress …

I hadn't *looked* at another man, let alone made love. Or had I?

I'd looked at Marcel. Yes, alright, I'd *looked*. But even when he'd come down to the cellar and kissed me, I'd felt guilty. Felt guilty that I'd enjoyed that fleeting moment. But I would *never* have dreamt of sleeping with someone else so soon. Not while my heart was taken. David, on the other hand, appeared to have been working hard at it! And *who* was the woman he was finally finding fulfillment with?

I wiped back tears of rage, swiping angrily at my cheeks.

Whoever she was, I *hated* her.

I ran up the stairs, hurtling past Axel Blanchard. Florence was on the landing, coming out of her westerly wing.

'Your father telephoned while you were out,' she said. 'It sounded important. Use my phone in here and ring him back.'

Florence looked at my red eyes but said nothing. She pointed to the open door of her study. I didn't want to call home now, but with Florence watching there was no choice.

Dad answered on the first ring. He must have been waiting by the phone.

The day couldn't get any worse.

'It's your grandmother,' he said. 'She died this morning.'

I'd begged my grandmother to let me live with her as soon as I could talk and had eked out as much happiness from a miserable childhood as I could at her red-brick terrace in Macclesfield. My mother had been relieved to let me go and my father (although we were close) was rarely home long enough to mind. Once, when my parents came to retrieve me, after a whole summer at Gran's home, they had found me hiding in the linen chest, curled up with the sheets, willing them to go away.

Gran's home was a place of cupboards and drawers, each one filled with the past. I liked to 'root', as she said, finding a never-ending source of treasures to restore to the light: a piece of jewellery, a box of elegant buttons, an old leather purse, or a rabbit's foot for luck. When the sun spliced the grey clouds above the derelict line of factory roofs, we sat on yellow Formica chairs in a scrap of garden at the back, squished in between a patch of rhubarb and her favourite orange rose. Gran smoked one of her Benson & Hedges, watching her freshly washed sheets billow on the line, pinned up high by a row of dolly pegs by her capable hands.

She told me stories of her ten siblings and how they'd slept head to toe in the same beds, in a tiny two-up two-down, in a rural village eighteen miles away. She hadn't wanted to come to this factory town where her husband had found work driving a lorry for a silk mill. She'd sickened at first, taking the bus home every night travelling there and back to see her mum and dad and her first-born daughter whom she'd been forced to leave behind. Eventually she was worn down. Her health was suffering, and her younger children neglected. There was no choice and so she took the bus back to Macclesfield for the last time and remained there for over forty years, on a quiet spot in St Andrew's road just opposite the church; a red-brick semi with painted glass tulips on the windows, buffed from top to bottom, and shiny as the brass button in her special tin.

As a child, Gran told me tales of a vibrant world full of people I longed to meet, and I begged her to take me there. I didn't know that the past was dead. How could it be, when it felt more alive than the starched bungalow in which my parents lived? The rag and bone man, the light-putter-outer, the shit-shoveller and the man who sold the donkey stones. These were the characters I knew and loved. I had no friends of my own. No pets or even a brother at that stage, though even when he came, he would not stay with us for long.

There was no mystery in my parents' home and little love lost between them. No stories or curios to touch; nothing to help you climb into the past. At my parents' house, everything was scrubbed within an inch of its life, and anything old was put into the bin. There were no old books or papers, no black and white pictures to tell a tale. The drawers were empty of those special purses and boxes of jewellery with their costume rubies and emeralds. My days at my parents' house were spent keeping out of the way, curled up with a book, trying not to make a mess.

And my question was always the same: When can I go to Gran's?
Gran was different. She put a drop of whisky in my

tea before school 'to fight the morning cold'. Or tied threads of golden wool to the top of my head because I wanted long princess hair. Gran was the one who came to my school gates with a felt hedgehog in a basket, because she knew I was missing him. Because she knew I was not yet happy at the big school.

At weekends, we went to the park to watch men bowl and talked of death: who'd died of what ailment or who'd moved where. Charlie had had a brain haemorrhage, Albert was lost in the war, Auntie Alice had gone to Blackpool to run a guesthouse. Worst of all Gran's eldest daughter had died of a big lump that had swelled up in her stomach – somewhere *down there*. They'd thought she was pregnant again, late on in life, with her third child. There'd been cause for celebration but then it turned out there was no baby and a few months later she had died.

There was a lot of talk about death. But I didn't mind. The dead felt as alive as the living to me. I knew none of them and yet I loved them all.

Gran's first daughter Edna had died four months after I was born in 1968. I must have been a comfort to my Gran at that time. She told me she'd still see Edna in the garden, standing by the fence, watching over her mam and dad. She saw her as clearly as I saw blackbirds pecking for worms in the early morning dew.

I asked my Gran when she would die. I wanted to count out the days we had left with Swan Vestas matches. I wanted to place them on the tea tray where we rolled our clay animals and to see how many there were. Like when we counted the days for Christmas, only worse. The worst there could possibly be.

'Don't worry,' she said. 'I promise I won't go till you're grown up and wed.'

I was nowhere near ready to be wed, and yet she had gone. I loved a man who was shagging women in grass skirts on a tropical island while trying to work out if he was enjoying it.

Gran couldn't die. I wasn't ready. I hadn't grown up. I hadn't said goodbye. I'd promised never to leave her alone in care, but always to look after her and be there. But I'd been *here*, in Paris, in a house far away, with three strange children, looking after them instead.

I threw open the door to my bedroom. Blinded by tears, it took me a moment to see that I couldn't throw myself on my bed to howl into the covers as I wanted to. There was something wrong. The bed was lying on its back with its legs in the air like a dead cockroach. The room was perfectly neat and tidy but everything had been turned upside down; my chairs, my desk, the objects on it, even the postcards I'd pinned to the hessian wall.

I slumped to the floor, next to a pile of shoes. They were shiny with egg white, broken shells slotted neatly into each one. Outside the door I heard giggling. It opened slowly and Delphine stuck her long white face around the jamb. Her eyes were sparkling. It was the first time I'd seen her look so excited. Clémence and Baptiste were behind her. She stopped, surprised to see me looking so upset. The children crept in one by one and came to sit by me on the floor. Clémence slipped her arms around me and gave me a kiss on the cheek, Delphine took my hand in hers, squeezed it briefly and then let it drop. Baptiste sat a little way off on the carpet, looking as if he might cry. They must have thought my grief had been brought on by their antics. I hadn't the energy to explain to them what this was about.

'We are sorry,' Delphine said. 'We don't want you to go.'

It felt strange being held by them; strange to be the adult. I saw myself, lying as a child with my head on my grandmother's pink crimplene dress, and started to sob again. I wasn't the child any more. The next generation was pushing its way up.

Life is a casting off.

It was a line I remembered from a play. Linda says it in *Death of a Salesman*.

Life *is* a casting off, and it had begun with the death of the person I most dreaded losing. It was also the day when I needed to cast away my last foolish dreams of David, the man to whom I'd given my heart without a second thought.

CHAPTER 11

Florence offered me time off work but I didn't go to gran's funeral though I regretted this bitterly later on. My family thought I didn't care. *Living it up in Paris.* That's what they said. The truth was I was too devastated to face it and felt too guilty to go. I should have been home to visit Gran, but I'd been wrapped up first in university and then with David. What was the point now she was dead? I'd let her down and I hated myself for it.

Years later this is still one of my life's biggest regrets. I learnt that she'd asked for me at the end, when the clouds had shifted and her memory returned just before death.

'Where's Karen?' she'd said, opening her eyes suddenly and formulating the question quite clearly.

On a wild goose chase, pursuing a man who didn't want me; trying to slot into another family … one that didn't matter. I'd been too afraid to face the thought of losing her and had broken the first promise I'd ever made to a person I loved – to be there at the end.

Gran hadn't lasted long. Once removed from the anchor of her home, death had come quickly.

She died of Alzheimer's disease, though no-one had bothered to tell me of her diagnosis at the time. She passed away in a hospital that would later be turned into a block of luxury flats.

My uncle went to the house, and though my grandfather was still alive, he threw away the things I still long to have kept. Even today. Nothing of value: the old leather purse where she saved my pocket money, the heavy post-war furniture no-one wants these days, the fake silver tea-caddy with the red lining – stage props to the happiest days of my childhood; objects that meant nothing to anyone else. Old tat. That's what they called it. Though a lifetime later if I could find each and every item in life's lost property cupboard, I would set each one back in place, piece by piece. I have dreamt of buying the house again, and of peeling back the carpets, the wallpaper, lifting the cement on the drive, to find a single trace of her again.

With anyone who moves to another country, there is always a sense of guilt. I followed the path of my own life, though however exciting my adventures were, this was the price I would pay. Gran pined a lifetime for her country village although it was only half an hour down the road. Yet without a car, and not knowing how to drive, she may as well have been at the other end of the world. Her sisters stayed in the same row of cottages until they died. In the place I know she longed to be.

Years later I found the cottage where she was born. It

was barely big enough to swing a cat. I wondered if one needed to travel so far to find happiness after all. Between them, Gran's sisters knew only a handful of lanes and a couple of farms, but they knew where they belonged, whereas part of me was always searching.

Wrapped up in grief, the days slipped by. Daylight hours were spent in The Submarine, ironing and listening to Radio 4. When evening came and dinner was done, I crept down to Jessica's garden cottage, where we drank cheap red wine from screw-top plastic bottles until it stained our tongues purple and made our breath reek. We snacked on day-old baguette and portions of garlic cheese – the only thing I ever found in Jessica's fridge. She begged me to bring a doggy-bag down from the main house and sulked if I didn't. She wasn't averse to sneaking up to the house when Florence was out at physio, filling her bag with biscuits or pieces of fruit and sneaking back across the lawn like one of *The Borrowers*.

We'd been in and out of Paris on a limited budget and taken to hanging out in a small restaurant off the Place du Tertre, owned by a man called Jacques. We couldn't afford to eat, so we ordered wine and pretended we'd had dinner, filling up on the bowl of complimentary peanuts from the bar. Eventually, out of the kindness of his heart, Jacques took to giving us scraps of bread and leftover rations from the *plat du jour*. Typically this consisted of a portion of mashed potato, a cluster of skinny French fries and a slither of *bavette à l'échalotte*. I wondered if these were the bits of meat left over on customers' plates, such was his generosity. The main course was followed by a bowl of *crème brûlée*, with incinerated sugar on the top. We were unable to communicate much in return. He grinned, revealing a set of short but even teeth, like a row of tiles on a Scrabble board.

Jacques employed two men in the restaurant. One a sporty looking man called Mathias who arrived and left the restaurant in a purple tracksuit. During working hours, like most waiters in Paris, he wore a smart pair of black trousers and a white shirt with a black apron knotted at the back, slipping into the tracksuit out of hours. We'd nicknamed him 'Tracker'. The other was a gangly, pale man by the name of Yannick. If he wasn't anaemic, he must have been a medical miracle, such was the transparency of his skin. The two men were drawn time and again to our table. We couldn't always understand what they said, but Jessica encouraged them, conscious that this was the only place in Paris where we could get a decent meal for free. Jessica wasn't interested in either of the waiters, but it suited her purposes to pretend she might be. She had a steely sense of 'needs-must' at times. She never crossed the line, but was expert at pretending she *just might*, when hungry. I was still grieving too much over my loss of Gran and David to care and had no appetite.

The real reason we visited Montmartre was Jessica's obsession with Samuel Beckett, or 'Sammy' as she called him. She had heard he sometimes ate *chez* Jacques, as well as drinking at the bar around the corner, so we were on red alert. Jacques' restaurant, Le Tartempion, was just off the Place du Tertre, in the shadow of the Sacre Coeur. The basilica loomed above us, its giant domes towering over the city, crisp and white like giant meringues. From the terrace, we were a stone's throw from the artists, spinning off their usual caricatures of tourists, and touting for trade as we passed by: *Mademoiselle, un petit portrait? Vous êtes anglaise?* They knew we were English before we'd opened our mouths: Jessica was still white as candle wax; I'd turned pink in the sun. I didn't know if it was our skin, our hair or our teeth that gave us away – the French always claim the English have rabbit teeth and big gums – but they always guessed our origins. Maybe we just looked wet behind the ears.

I was in the kitchen making the children's dinner. Jessica and I were planning the coming weekend and wondering what to do. She wanted to visit Le Musée Rodin, whereas I fancied travelling out to Versailles to see the Hall of Mirrors and walking in the park.

We were debating the merits of both plans when Florence entered the kitchen.

'Bonsoir, les filles,' she said turning to address me. I prepared myself to receive orders for one of her usual tasks. It was drum night and I imagined that there would be a long list of things needing doing in her absence. To my horror, she announced that the next day was the last day of school and the start of the Big Summer Holidays. *Les grandes vacances.* I should have known, but I'd been so wrapped up

in my misery of late, that I'd completely forgotten, having also pushed to the back of my mind Bonne-Maman's threats to take us away to the family château. This was likely to mean six long weeks shut up with the children in the countryside, and little chance of escape into my thoughts, or even The Submarine. I couldn't even use my French classes at L'institut Catholique as an excuse, as these were not due to start until September. There was no escape.

Florence announced her plans without further ado. 'Bonne-Maman will arrive late morning. She will be taking you and the children to Trémouillet.'

'Where's that again?' I asked, not liking the fact that I could be moved at any time, like a chess piece, according to the will of the players.

'It's about three hours from here. It's my mother's family home. The children love it. There are woods and wild things in the park. It is a little derelict, you understand. We only use it in the summer, but you will have everything you need and the weather should be good, *n'est-ce pas?*'

'Are you coming?' I asked, hoping she had changed her plans.

Florence laughed. '*Mais non.* How I would love to have this luxury, but Marcel needs me for the final stage of works to my *atelier*, and I cannot leave poor Axel to fend for himself.'

Remembering that Jessica was in the room, Florence turned to her, lest she thought she had been forgotten.

'Jessica, it would be nice while the children are away, if you could help prepare Axel's dinner. I think the garden has had enough, how do you say, *snip-snipping* for the moment. It is looking like a sheep when its wool has been, how do you say, *rasé?* Shorn, is that it? Yes, shorn. Perhaps you could turn your attentions to the house while your friend is away?'

Jessica gave her a tight smile. I knew she was quite content *snip-snipping* in the garden while reading her book. I'd seen how she positioned her chair beneath the trees to read, reaching an indolent arm upwards for a lazy clip of a twig, before turning her page. There was nothing strenuous about Jessica's form of gardening. I was curious to know how she would get on starching shirts and pairing up socks. Hearing my friend's list of chores, I felt a sudden surge of excitement. I was going away! It might be quite exciting after all. And what's more, I'd be living the high life in a château, and seeing a different part of France. I should buy a travel diary so I could write up my adventures. Things were looking up. Cinderella *would* go to the ball!

The next morning I was surprised to see a gleaming cherry-red hatchback roar up outside the wrought-iron gates. I'd grown so used to seeing Bonne-Maman arrive on her clanking bicycle, that I'd not imagined that she would be driving anything quite so top of the range. In my mind, she was the batty old lady from *Bedknobs and Broomsticks*, and I'd have been less surprised if she'd pitched up on a flying broomstick.

Her hair was rolled into a neat little silver-grey bun

comme d'habitude, and she wore a sensible summer blouse and skirt, with flat sandals. Around her neck hung a sturdy crucifix, the only piece of jewellery visible. There wasn't a scrap of make-up on her face, not even a little *rouge,* as Gran would have said.

The children were lined up obediently in the hallway. They marched to the car in single file, kissing their mother on the cheek as they exited. Florence clambered down the stone steps, using the hand rail to help her, calling to me to fetch a bottle of water from the kitchen for the journey. I turned back into the house just as the phone started ringing. Florence was already out in the street by the car. It would be impossible for her to swing her way back in time to pick up. With some hesitation, I lifted the receiver and spoke into the headset, imitating the way I had heard Florence speak.

'*Oui bonjour, qui est à l'appareil?*'

I heard a voice, which although French, sounded familiar.

'*Bonjour, comment ça va?*'

For a wild, heart-wrenching moment, I thought it was David. He'd seen sense and had called to rescue me and take me far away! But then as the man continued speaking, I realised it couldn't be my ex-boyfriend, or he would have switched to English by now. The caller repeated a form of his earlier question.

'*Tout va bien?*'

'*Oui, très bien merci. Je vais chercher Florence.*'

There was a silence and I wondered if I'd formed my sentence properly. In desperation, I repeated it again slowly in English.

'Just a minute. I will go and get Florence.'

'*Mais non, ça va bien.* Not Florence. *Attendez un instant.*'

The call must be for Axel. But he was out too. At this point the caller had clearly had enough of not being understood, and in hesitant English said:

'Do you like tea?'

'Yes,' I said, surprised, '*bien sûr.*'

'You will take tea with me then? Tomorrow? High above Paris. We shall drink tea together in the air. On a roof top.'

The man laughed, as if realising these were not the right words. As he laughed I realised who it was. It was Marcel, the architect and bean-sucking guest; the man who had come down to the cellar to kiss me, when he should have been drinking coffee with Florence and Hugo.

The car horn beeped impatiently. Bonne-Maman was chomping at the bit. She wanted to turn the magic knob of her automobile and lift us high above the rooftops of the western suburbs of Paris.

But I didn't want to go with her. I wanted to drink tea in Paris with Marcel.

'I have to go,' I said into the receiver. '*Je dois partir.*' 'You are too busy? *Quel dommage.*'

There was a pause before he blurted out a stream of French which was so fast I couldn't catch it. Later I deciphered the words one by one.

'*Je vous donne rendez-vous au café de la Samaritaine. Sur le toit du magasin. Demain si vous voulez. A 16h. Vous ne travaillez pas les samedis, je crois?*'

I could answer the last part of the sentence easily enough. No, I didn't usually work on Saturdays, but no, I couldn't meet him on the roof top of the shop he was suggesting. Wherever this *La Samaritaine* place was, I must go to the château with the children. I couldn't find the words I needed to explain. The car horn beeped again, and the phone clicked off at the other end. Marcel had gone.

I told Florence it was a wrong number, though I'm not sure why. One thing was sure: Marcel wasn't looking for the mistress of the house. He'd clearly said so. Even my French was good enough to have picked that up. Instinctively I knew that Florence would not like her luncheon guest and the artistic genius behind her creative space, calling to invite her domestic help for a secret cup of tea on a Paris rooftop.

At times, I suspected that Florence sent me down to the cellar to iron *on purpose* when Marcel came to the house. On occasions, he popped over to see her alone, carrying great long scrolls of papers covered with fine line drawings. At other times, he was accompanied by scowling Hugo. Florence had not renewed her initial invitation to share lunch together and Marcel had not repeated the experience of sneaking down to The Submarine for a kiss. I always knew when there was to be a luncheon with the men. Florence advised me to make a quick salad, explaining that she would need the kitchen later. *Alone* was what she really meant. When the doorbell rang, I disappeared into the cellar without a trace; a stage-hand who must never be seen.

The previous week Marcel had rung the bell when I was on my way underground. I opened the door and he gave me a kiss on each cheek. Florence appeared from out of nowhere, crossing the space between us with giant leaps on her crutches. She pointed to a washing basket at the bottom of the stairs and asked me quite sharply if I would take it down and start my work. I had been in the process of doing precisely this. Florence knew it. It was an exercise in boundaries. These were the minefields which must be avoided daily when sharing a house with another woman. It was akin to being bridesmaid at a wedding – never a good idea to outshine the bride. One must be useful but never indispensable, discreet yet always available, and most importantly, god forbid, never an object of desire.

Aware of both Marcel and Florence's watchful gaze, I'd picked up my washing basket that day, my eyes filling with tears at the sharp prick of loneliness. It didn't take much since Gran's death. Later when her guests had left, Florence called down to me from the top of the cellar steps and invited me up to drink camomile tea with her on the cold white sofa, next to the penis sculpture. I think she felt guilty and was trying to make it up to me with a cup of tepid gnat's piss.

Now, ensconced in the back seat of Bonne-Maman's car, I thought about the phone call, playing Marcel's words over in my mind as I watched the suburbs of Paris slip away beneath Bonne-Maman's capable hands, concrete and tarmacadam blurring into long stretches of green. We shot along at great speed, the roads free of traffic cones or roadworks. Once past the tollgate to the south of Paris, we barely saw another car on the road.

Bonne-Maman was a confident driver, clutching the steering wheel with delicate hands, her long slender legs, which barely reached the ground, banging at the pedals. Under her watchful gaze, the children were surprisingly disciplined. Delphine and Baptiste read their comic books quietly; *Gaston Lagaffe* or *Tintin*, Clémence sucked her thumb until she fell asleep with her head resting on Delphine's shoulder. Squinting at the road ahead and hunched over the enormous steering wheel, Bonne-Maman paid little attention to any of us. I don't think she wanted to talk. She didn't seem particularly interested in me, and knowing that she had taken this same trip every summer with an ever-changing series of nannies, I understood why.

We drove south for three hours into the middle of France. Not to the south of France of my dreams – Nice, Monaco or Aix – but to a land-locked village in the middle of nowhere in a part of France no-one ever mentions much.

We pulled off the motorway and stopped for lunch at La Courte Paille – a round restaurant with a straw roof. There was an open fire in the corner and I ordered a steak which the chef sizzled over the open flames, my vegetarian days now completely forgotten. The children had chicken nuggets and chips and argued over the free plastic toys. Bonne-Maman nipped neatly at a goat's cheese salad sprinkled with honey and, declining dessert, drank a small shot of black coffee. I fancied an ice cream, but didn't like to order it. I reminded myself that I was not one of the children, though having spent a morning in this dominant woman's presence I felt like one.

Holidays as a child had been few and far between and dependent on the stand-by tickets Dad got on the cheap from work. We were never quite sure if we would board a plane, and the start of our holidays usually saw us sitting on our cases at Manchester airport with Dad running from terminal to terminal like a harassed hare sweating red-faced in his best suit. Sometimes we arrived in Spain on different flights; once my mother travelled to Alicante in the cockpit.

Back in Bonne-Maman's car, we continued along the road for a further forty minutes. I was dozing off when the car slowed down and made a sharp left turn, before bumping down a long dirt track. The children woke with excited cries of: '*On est là, on est là!*'

The avenue to the château stretched before us, cutting through a long line of oaks with fields to each side. It was a stretch of the imagination to pretend that anyone other than royalty would have such a long driveway in the UK. It twisted and turned for several hundred metres before the house appeared on the horizon. The beaten track beneath the car tyres was rough and perilous, the sodden earth punctured with giant pock marks. There had clearly been a recent downpour although in Paris it had been dry for weeks. A hawk perched on an electric wire, barely flinching as we passed. The telegraph pole was tilted at an angle, the wire sagging dangerously low along the ditch in which a flow of water babbled noisily. Judging from the fallen trees by the side of the track, there had been a recent storm. As we proceeded a family of partridge waddled in front of the car; three chicks following their mother into the field.

At the end of the drive the road opened out into a small clearing. The property was hidden by a stone wall which ran around the outside. A small wooden bridge on a chain had been lowered down over the ditch. It *was* a proper castle then, with ramparts and a moat.

We crossed the rickety wooden bridge and parked in front of the castle. The straw and lime walls were scored by dark oak beams. The house leant against the barn, a more recent addition, driven by the weight of the years. Despite its name, and the frills of its drawbridge entrance, I was disappointed to discover that Château de Trémouillet was a wattle and daub manor house of reasonable proportions, and not a rambling Gothic castle with turrets.

An old man in braces was sweeping the pathway. Bonne-Maman parked the car and he came over to shake her hand, pushing the green cap back from his sweaty red forehead. The man said something and pointed to the house. A woman emerged from the doorway, rubbing wet hands on her blue apron.

Bonne-Maman introduced me to the couple as *la nounou*, or 'the nanny'. She didn't bother with my name. 'She is English,' she said, excusing me in advance. I shook hands with the guardians, whose names were Monsieur and Madame Villard, though they pressed me to call them Jacques and Yvonne. The children ran off to see the park. I wanted to follow them, but reined myself in. Bonne-Maman informed me that she would show me the house, after which I could bring in the children's bags, unpack their clothing and help prepare dinner.

The rough stone floor of the hallway was cold beneath my feet. It was a dark house and it took my eyes a second to adjust. Vlad would have loved it. Shivering, I wondered if I should have brought some warm clothes. The house had an autumnal feel that called for a roaring log fire and a pair of fur-lined slippers to combat the chill rising from the thick stone floors. The skirting boards were encrusted with mould, which was hardly surprising as there was no sign of any central heating, just an open fireplace in the kitchen, infusing the air with a damp and acrid smell. The kitchen was a sparse and utilitarian space, devoid of any modern appliances, and divided in half by a long oak table. The original stone sink was slung low against the wall in the corner designed for a shorter generation but perfect for Yvonne, who was as short and stout as a baby troll.

On the fireplace above the chimney, a faded olive branch adorned a simple cross. Sitting at an angle beside it there was an old black-and-white wedding photograph of a couple in late nineteenth-century clothing. The bride and groom were complimentary in size and appearance like a pair of identical twins, with only the dress and the bonnet to differentiate between *Monsieur* and *Madame*. The bride's face was painfully unattractive, her dark eyes bleak beneath her heavy forehead and caterpillar brows. She had the kind of chin which would look better with a beard. Madame

Villard followed my gaze and made the sign of the cross. '*Mes parents*,' she said fondly, and then in French: 'They worked here all their lives.' My heart went out to them. Bonne-Maman pursed her lips at this interruption and we moved quickly on.

Beyond the kitchens I was pleased to see that the château allowed itself a little *grandeur*. The first floor was enchanting, with nothing to disappoint. The hallway was lined with bookshelves and paintings of the family. The subjects depicted were blessed with a far better morphology than Madame Villard's ancestors. There was an exquisite oval portrait of Florence's grandmother, glancing down at us with those same unmistakable doe eyes and long dark hair which framed her pale face. It was a perfect portrayal of Florence minus the bongo drums and the baggy pantaloons.

The children had private rooms, each as pretty as a picture, with four-poster beds piled high with pillows and set into decorative alcoves. The furnishings were plush, with antique desks and cupboards, chiming clocks and gilt mirrors bedecked with angels. Just like Versailles! We had left the sixteenth-century stone kitchen on the ground floor behind us, and had risen in rank to the eighteenth century, with rooms as plush as those in which Marie-Antoinette had lounged in *Le Petit Trianon*.

Bonne-Maman opened the door to show me her room – '*Should you need me in the night ...*' – before turning up the stairs to the second floor. It was considerate of her, I thought, to have allowed me my privacy far from

162

the children. For a second, I warmed to the old lady. Admittedly the second floor was not quite as *grand* as the one below, but it was comfortably furnished all the same. The rooms overlooked the park at a higher level, and in the distance, I observed the russet smudge of deer on the horizon. There was a nursery with a rocking horse and a doll's house with period furniture in miniature and one of those terrifying life-sized dolls on the bed with a porcelain face, a black petticoat dress and wide staring eyes.

'My favourite room as a child,' Bonne-Maman said. 'There are still toys here from my grandparents' day. The castle has been in the family since before the Revolution.' We continued, heading towards a narrow staircase at the end of the hallway and up a third set of stairs. The third-floor ceilings were low, and I was forced to duck my head beneath the beams. At the end of the corridor there was a small wooden door.

'*Voilà, votre chambre.*' I noticed how the children's grandmother insisted on using the polite French form of *vous*, whereas with Florence the friendlier form of *tu* was acceptable.

Surprisingly there wasn't a room on the other side of the door as I expected, but a steep flight of wooden stairs leading to a fourth floor. The stairs were not made of the same elm or oak as the lower stairs, but from rough planks of wood that had been nailed together like the bottom of cargo crates.

'*Allez-y,*' she waved impatiently, and pushed me forwards with a hard poke in the back. I climbed the stairs, realising halfway up that Bonne-Maman had abandoned me. The stairs opened onto another corridor, no more than two or three metres long. The wooden ceiling slats had sagged, clumps of plaster hung down precariously, wafting in a persistent draught which came from somewhere above my head. The corridor was so tight my shoulders rubbed against the walls on each side, dislodging the blistering lead paint from the swollen pulp which mascaraded as dividing walls.

Hunting for my room was akin to receiving a birthday present in a huge box and tearing off layer upon layer of paper in excitement, only to find a disappointingly small box at the very bottom. One in which there would never be a diamond.

My room in the attic was *une chambre de bonne* – or maid's room. Every bourgeois house in France has at least one, and this was mine. I lifted the latch of an ill-fitting door and found myself in a cupboard. The room was barely wide enough for a single bed. The walls were gnawed with damp, and flakes of lead paint speckled the old grey cover on the bed. The base of the bed was covered with an itchy-looking layer of sack-cloth or ticking. The mattress was lumpy and uneven and smelt of wee. The bed looked as if it had been requisitioned from Bedlam, with iron bars top and tail. It had been designed for shorter people than mankind has produced in the last three hundred years. There was a crucifix above the bed on which an agonized figure of Jesus writhed in pain, the sculptor having spared the onlooker none of Christ's suffering. In the corner, there was a small enamel sink, above which hung a mottled mirror on a chain. The mouse droppings around the taps confirmed my worst fears.

Paltry light trickled into the room from the skylight above. Rain drops flecked the glass as the sky darkened beyond the grime of the window pane. They trickled down the ancient lead frame, dripping down the wall. No wonder the bed was sodden.

I flicked at an ancient light switch. The single bulb above the bed hissed a moment, the circuit struggling to connect through the humid wires.

'*Dépêchez-vous*,' Bonne-Maman called from the bottom of the stairs. 'You have work to do!'

CHAPTER 12

Despite the summer shower, the children had disappeared off into the woods wearing their brightly coloured plastic raincoats and boots. I wanted to follow them, drawn to a slither of light on the horizon and the parkland beyond, but my attempt at escape was curtailed by Bonne-Maman's sinewy yet insistent frame, as she sidled between me and the doorway and guided me back to the kitchen.

'*Pourriez-vous aider notre cuisinière?*' she said, pointing towards the kitchen. *Could you help our cook?* Yvonne's ancestors might have lived on the chimney for the past fifty years, but she was still referred to by her profession and not her maiden name.

Yvonne's sleeves were rolled up as she bent over the scrubbed pine table, gripping a dead bird between rheumatic fingers. The air was thick with the smell of wet feathers and bird poop, the floor covered with brown feathers. The bird was only half-plucked, lending it a tragi-comic 'thespian in brown britches' look. Yvonne continued to snatch clusters of feathers from the body with short rhythmic tearing sounds. Satisfied at last, she stepped back to survey the now naked bird.

'*A vous,*' she said encouragingly, and offered me a sharp-looking knife from the rack.

I stared in horror. The only meat I'd ever had to deal with had come shrink-wrapped from the supermarket, plucked and smooth, its baby-pink skin devoid of feathers. I couldn't pluck a dead bird while it looked me in the eye ... not after owning a budgie all those years.

'I'm sorry,' I said, 'I can't. I don't know what to do.' Bonne-Maman cocked her head, her small and glint-

ing eyes scanning my face. She looked ready to fly at me. There was something avian about Bonne-Maman herself, with those crinkled white patches beneath her eyes and her claw-like hands.

'*Et alors,* what is the meaning of this nonsense?' she said firmly. '*À la campagne* – in the country – we do not have time for such *manières.*'

In other words, there was no time for my pussy-footing around. I had to tear birds' flesh.

Yvonne stared at me kindly. '*Je vais vous montrer,*' she said, and raised the dead bird from the table, her forefinger and thumb nipping the dead flesh. She pointed to a series of dark red dots, then taking the knife cut into the flesh, exposing a layer of yellow fat beneath the skin. She prodded with the tip, until with a grunt of satisfaction she'd extracted a small black pellet like a military surgeon.

'*BERK!*' She spat on the floor to show me how disgusting

it was and said something about the official hunting season being closed, but that luckily nobody on the estate bothered about details like that. They could blast birds from the sky 'til their hearts burst at Château de Trémouillet.

Before long Yvonne had removed three pellets from the carcass and was satisfied. Taking up her knife again, she proceeded to cut a circular slit around the bird's anus. Once the incision was in place the intestines slipped forwards and out onto the table. I gagged and averted my eyes, certain I'd throw up, the smell of wet bird and acrid soot turning my stomach.

Unable to face the bird's despairing look of humiliation a moment longer, I ran out of the back door and retched. I was not going to pluck and prepare pheasant. No way! The glossy advert in *The Lady* magazine had mentioned none of this. I'd already checked out the forms that Jessica had received from the au-pair agency detailing what a family could (and could not) ask their hired help to do: light household duties, yes; ironing the children's clothes, yes – my family were already in breach of contract with the enforced ironing of Axel's shirts. There was, however, no mention anywhere of having to touch slippery intestines.

I sought consolation by the compost heap, oblivious to the rain, revelling in the scent of rich soil and freshly cut grass. After a few minutes, I felt strong enough to return to the house, ready to have it out with Bonne-Maman. I'd happily go home if I must. I'd tell Florence and Axel I couldn't stand it anymore. Anyway, what was the point of staying on now that David had gone?

Back inside Bonne-Maman was reading *Le Figaro* in the sitting room, peering through owlish spectacles perched on the end of her pinched nose. The children were colouring in their art-pads at a round table by the window. They were so busy with what they were doing that they didn't look up. Did they even need a *jeune fille au pair*?

'I'm here,' I said. 'Sorry about that. Felt a bit green.' Bonne-Maman had lit a small wooden fire in the grate.

The air was chilly, revealing an underlying layer of must which the smoking logs did little to abate. Outside the window there were flashes of lightning on the horizon and black clouds scudding up towards the house. A big storm was brewing by the look of things. Summer had forgotten to make an appearance at Château de Trémouillet.

It must nearly be time for *le goûter*. My stomach had acclimatised over the past few weeks to the French tradition of a big snack at four o'clock, and I was starting to feel peckish, despite the lunchtime feast of steak and chips. I wondered if Bonne-Maman would give me instructions to rustle something up. If she didn't say anything soon I'd ask if I could go down to the kitchen and lay a tray of treats for the children, carefully adding a portion for myself.

I coughed, to remind the grandmother of my presence. The old lady made me wait, taking her time and reading to the end of her article before deigning to look up. I watched the flames dancing in the grate as they tried to take hold of the wood and started to feel sleepy. It was cardigan season, if not thermal undie weather in this neck of the woods. I hadn't felt so cold since leaving Wales. I shivered, edging instinctively towards the fire. Bonne-Maman was wearing a woollen cardigan over her chemise and a thick-looking Hermès scarf. I, on the other hand, had brought an optimistic bag of summer wear for my trip, and still wore the skimpy spotted dress that I had chosen back in Paris that morning. In thin cotton, it 'fit where it touched' as my inner-mother whispered disparagingly, but had felt perfect for the South of France. I wondered if Delphine could lend me a jumper. I might be able to stretch one a bit.

Realising that Bonne-Maman had finally spoken, I tuned back in. Hopefully she had understood about the pheasant plucking. If she found me another task, I'd willing put heart and soul into it, so long as it didn't involve snipping at a bird's anus.

'Ahh,' she said, 'I see you have a little colour back. You were white as *paracetamol*. Now, if I understand correctly, you do not wish to help Yvonne with our pheasants. No? I thought not. Well, if you are ready, I will show you how else you may be of service, since the birds have proved too much, *n'est-ce pas?*'

Bonne-Maman was up on her dainty feet before I could think what she meant. I followed her out of the door, passing Yvonne who was on her way in with a large tray laden with tea and cake. I twisted my neck and observed as she set the tray down on the table before the children. On it, there was a pot of tea, a carton of orange juice, a mound of butter and a bowl of strawberry jam. Not to mention the pièce de résistance, a brioche of gigantic proportions exploding like sugared lava from its tin, the odour of freshly baked bread tingeing the dank air with its promise of goodness. My stomach contorted in anticipation.

'*J'arrive!*' Bonne-Maman sang out cheerfully to her grandchildren.

My heart plummeted. Surely, regardless of the mission I was to embark on, there was time for tea? If we were gone too long, knowing the children's ferocious appetites, there'd be nothing left.

I followed Bonne-Maman to a different part of the house where most of the furniture was covered in dust sheets. The house had separate wings, just like Manderley. I'd read *Rebecca* enough times in our small handkerchief of a bungalow to dream of houses with eastern and western wings, and closed off areas which lay ghostly and still.

We climbed to the top of the house, using yet another staircase. The architect who had designed Château de Trémouillet was clearly obsessed with levels. When we reached the top Bonne-Maman opened a curved door. Beyond it, there was a round room with a domed ceiling. A bird flew from a beam and circled the room before exiting through a small hole in the wall. A swallow perhaps. There was the sound of a fly buzzing – more than one; several dozen maybe. The ceiling stretched high above me, its beams shaped like the framework of an upturned boat. A large brass bell hung on a chain from the middle section. *Bien sûr!* We were in the bell tower or *le clocher*. There wasn't a window, and what little light there was crept in through the slats of wood in the ceiling, beneath the bare beams. The old lady switched on a single light bulb which hung down from a frayed cord.

Bonne-Maman was saying something I didn't understand and pointing at the floor. I looked down, still a little dizzy from gazing upwards. It took me a second to realise why the floor was black. Not just black, but crunchy. We were standing on several layers of dead flies. Some were still moving, most were frozen in death, iridescent wings pointing to the skies above. The bird circled above my head. I looked again. It wasn't a bird after all, but a bat with rubbery wings. A flying mouse to all intents and purposes. Several of its more indolent relatives were hanging beneath a beam in the corner, suspended over a pile of bat poo and something which, on closer inspection, might have been owl pellets. But I had only read of such things, so I couldn't be sure. My exposure to animal droppings had been limited to what I'd seen onscreen in David Attenborough programmes.

Bonne-Maman opened a cupboard in the corner and retrieved a broom, a metal pan and a roll of black bin liners.

'*Il faut nettoyer les mouches,*' she said.

It took a moment for her words to register. She shoved the brush into my hand to help the process. *Les mouches.* The word came back to me from the useful list of animals and insects at the back of my Collins dictionary. I'd spent a lot of time learning lists of animals, insects and birds

– ladybirds, robins and larks – when I should have been reading *The Faerie Queene*. This particular noun was not on the list of France's most whimsical creatures.

'You want me to clean *the flies*?' I said in horror. She grimaced firmly.

'*C'est ça. Vous avez bien compris.*'

It took over an hour to brush the dead flies and owl pellets into bin bags. I wondered when the room had last been swept; the bottom layer of insects was petrified inside a layer of ancestral bat droppings. The top layer of wings still retained the occasional flash of green and blue. One or two of the victims still clung to life, dying in my presence. The light grew paler as I heard the distant rumble of thunder. The rain beat hard against the roof tiles. The single bulb cast a paltry light. In a way, this was better. Looking at hundreds of dead corpses was disgusting. Surely it wasn't my job to do this, but I'd already refused to pluck pheasants. At least with the flies there wasn't any blood. I'd filled two bags full by the time I'd finished and I was frozen to the bone. The bell tower wasn't insulated and the wind had found an easy passage into the dome, creeping through the open wood slats, pricking my legs and arms with goose bumps. My skin was blue and my throat itched. I felt sick and needed a hot shower.

The brioche was finished by the time I went back downstairs, save a few sugared baubles which lay at the bottom of the tin. I put the rubbish bins into the shed at the bottom of the garden, as instructed by Yvonne. Her husband would take them to the *déchetterie* the next morning, along with the bags of intestines and pheasant heads. We were too far out in the countryside to have the luxury of refuse collectors.

On my return to the living room, my head was aching and my throat now felt as if I'd a jagged chicken bone stuck in it. I was shaking from the cold, and hadn't yet had time to find a jumper. The fire was still on, but the enormous oak log which squatted in the middle of the grate mocked the gentle lick of flames around its edge. It would take hours before there was any real heat. If ever.

My nose was dripping and I started to cough. There were shivers dancing the length of my spine, and my scalp was tingling in that way which spelt out certain illness of an infectious kind. The French have a lovely expression for it: they say you know when you are ill because you can count the hairs on your head. I knew this to be true, as a shiver entwined itself around the follicles of my scalp, like a stiff breeze through a field of corn.

I sat with the children a moment and tried to talk to them, but my French failed me.

Bonne-Maman saw my fatigue and tutted, as if I was shirking duty, and asked if I would go into the kitchen to help Yvonne. What could I do but obey? I rearranged my aching bones into a standing position.

Yvonne was kinder. She saw I looked unwell, and sat me down by her own crackling log fire. She placed a wrinkled hand on my forehead and fussed around me. Her husband was in the other chair, his head lolling forwards into his newspaper where he had fallen asleep.

'*Oh, la la!*' she exclaimed. '*Ça va pas! Vous avez attrapé la grippe.*'

Grippe. I remembered that word. It meant flu. Surely not?

'*Ça a dû être un courant d'air!*' ('It must have been a draught.')

Over the years, I would learn that the French had a terrible fear of draughts. These must be protected against at all odds and were feared as much as the bubonic plague. The slightest change in temperature had women reaching for little woollen throws or jackets. A draught was a terrible thing. It could kill you. It was the subject of much conversation. Was there one encroaching upon the room? Would there be one later? Had one imagined a draught brewing? Such questions demanded urgent attention and had whole parties of house guests frozen like retrievers, scouting for signs of the dreaded 'courant d'air'. I had been whipped by a thousand draughts up in that bloody bell tower and was feeling worse by the minute. Yvonne reached into a small corner cupboard and pulled out a bottle of Armagnac. She gave me a glass and motioned at me to head it, along with two paracetamols.

Bonne-Maman found me asleep in the chair half an hour later. She shook me, and I stirred from a feverish dream. There was a rapid fire of French between the two women and, before I could protest, I was told that I must go to bed. This was not the outcome I'd been hoping for, as Yvonne was busy dishing up the most delicious looking pheasant dinner. The same fellow she had plucked earlier that day and who had now assumed a more comestible and recognizable form. My previous disgust had vanished. The succulent pieces of meat, swathed in creamy mushroom sauce, slipping from serving spoon to bowl, appeared to have little connection with the beaks and heads in the bin. There was some argument between the two women as to whether I had a cold or the flu, and whether the right tactic was to starve my sickness or bring me up a tray and feed it. I was about to plead they feed it when Bonne-

Maman came to a decision and propelled me out of the room and up the stairs.

'*Allez vous coucher,*' she said. '*Vous avez besoin de dormir.*' They were going to starve it.

My chamber was worse than I remembered: smaller, narrower, colder. Surely a fresh batch of mice had been back to the room in my absence, pissing on the bed in protest at having to share their quarters. The smell was overpowering. The mattress squeaked and groaned with every turn. I needed to pee, but the bathroom was downstairs, and once I was in my bed I couldn't face moving again. I was still in my dress, realising that I hadn't brought a decent nightie. My head felt hot and dry, but my throat was itching, and my nose running. I didn't have any tissues. It was hell. In desperation, I would have blown it on the eiderdown, but it was too rough; rough as a badger's bum, as Gran would have said. I tried to swallow but the left side of my throat was painfully constricted. I didn't know how this infection could have taken hold of me so quickly, but it wasn't the first time. I had a feeble immune system. I wondered if it was because, like most children born in the late sixties, I'd been deprived of breast milk and bottlefed since birth. Whatever the reason, I had always been a sickly child. 'Born with a tissue in your hand!' Dad used to say. I wondered if French germs sought me out, knowing that I had little resistance to them. I'd grown accustomed to my own germs in England and Wales, but these were different, and I wasn't yet acclimatised.

I fell into an uneasy sleep in which there were rooms full of flies and pheasant heads, and I was trying to get out of the house to follow the yellow brick road back to civilisation, where I could meet Marcel for tea. But I didn't know where I was going, and in one dream when I finally pitched up at the tea-room in question, David was sitting there, drinking Earl Grey and eating scones with a girl in a grass skirt. She was incredibly beautiful, with long black hair and slender legs and arms that had been caressed by tropical sun. The only oddity about her was her nose; it was a bird's beak. She looked at me scornfully, running her eyes up and down my figure. I was dirty as a chimney sweep from cleaning a bell tower and I wasn't wearing any shoes.

In another dream, I was trying to run away from the Blanchard house. I wanted to pack my bags but every time I tried to do so, the contents spilled out. Finally, I climbed through the window and over the slate rooftops to escape. Jessica waved goodbye from the cool gardens of the cottage, clutching a gardenia and wearing a dainty white dress and straw hat. But when I finally arrived at the metro I stumbled upon Florence, who was squatting on the platform playing her drums, while Marcel stood behind her and kissed her neck, shadowed by an enormous poster of Axel Blanchard.

I dreamt time and again that I'd relieved myself down an alleyway in some backstreet Parisian *ruelle*, yet no matter how many times I emptied my bladder, it was still full. A voice in my dream told me that the mice had peed on my bed so, why couldn't I? *Let it seep out*, my inner devil whispered. *No-one will know.*

It was the burning need to pee which woke me. I needed to find a toilet, even if it meant creeping downstairs in the dark. Just then I heard it. Quite distinctly. Someone had walked across the room and turned on the tap of the small sink in the corner. I pulled myself awake, certain it was Yvonne come to bathe my head with a damp cloth. After all, I was very feverish. Perhaps they were worried I would die in the night and that they'd have to ship my body back to England. Perhaps she had brought me a little warm broth and freshly baked bread.

'Yvonne?' I whispered.

There was no reply, but the tap was gushing. I sat up and scrabbled for the light, but couldn't find it. I'd forgotten that it was hanging on a cord above my head. I stepped out of bed, shivering, though my naked feet felt hot on the rough wooden floorboards. I walked across the room with outstretched hands. The room was so small, it only took a couple of steps. There was no-one there, yet the tap was gushing merrily into the sink, the icy cold water causing my burning body to shudder violently.

I rushed back to the bed and pulled the covers over my head, still desperate to pee, but I needed to gather my strength before I could face going out into the corridor. Lying on my back in terror, I discerned a faint rent in the darkness through the skylight. There wasn't a full moon to light the sky, but now that the rain had finally stopped, the stars shed a faint glow in the inky night. I thought how beautiful they were, and how far we must be from civilisation for there to be no light pollution. An owl screeched on its late-night hunt. As I began to relax, pondering the mysteries of The Universe, I heard footsteps again. The door hadn't opened, and no-one had come into the room, and yet someone was walking next to me on the wooden boards.

A second later, and the tap was gushing into the basin like Niagra Falls. I drew my knees to my chin and ducked beneath the covers. There was someone in my room. The tap continued to pound the porcelain basin, as the footsteps made a distinctive pathway back towards the door. It must be the children. There was no other explanation. After all, they had been known to turn all the furniture in my room upside down. Surely they weren't above trying to scare their *jeune fille au pair* out of her wits.

I needed to find the light. I emerged from beneath the covers and groped along the wall. Nothing. The cord of the light-switch dangled in my face which was more than I could bear. I screamed, realising a split-second later what it was. I tugged the cord sharply and the bulb above my head flickered on. The room was empty.

The tap switched itself on three or four times more that night. I huddled up into a hot dry ball, limbs drawn up to my cheeks, fighting to swallow through a tousle of infected tonsils. I was sick but not deranged. This was not something I was *imagining*. Footsteps paced my floorboards throughout the night. I woke with a start at least three or four times to the sound of regular padding. The explanation was simple. There was a *ghost*.

I lay rigid imagining who the ghost might be, settling before dawn with absolute certainty on a French maid, whose fiancé had been killed by the English in the Hundred-Year War. I was sleeping in her bed, my nose dripping onto what must have been her sheets. It was clear she was not impressed.

It was about half past eight when I finally shivered my way to the kitchen certain that when Bonne-Maman saw how unfit I was for duty a doctor would be called. If she were anything like her daughter, medical assistance would be summoned *de toute urgence*. Florence *loved* doctors. Evenings were filled with rounds of visits for both herself and the children: *homéopathes, orthophonistes, kinésithérapeutes, physiothérapeutes, craniosacral masseurs* – appointments scrolled onto the calendar behind the kitchen door, though the family appeared fighting fit.

Throughout their lives my grandparents were terrified of disturbing the doctor for no good reason. As a child, they waited until my ear drum perforated before calling out a disgruntled stethoscope-wielding giant; the same man who ten years later reluctantly agreed to attend to my grandad's burst ulcer only once he lay in a pool of blood on his front-room floor. By French standards, the NHS was brutal.

Like most French women, Florence had no qualms in calling out the doctor, a battery of specialists, or even the emergency services, at the slightest twinge. The French popped in and out of the surgery with the ease of a child popping into the corner shop for a bag of sticky toffee. Doctors were there to serve and to obey, summoned to one's home at the slightest shiver to perform miracles, or at times to simply reassure.

Mother: '*Docteur*, I'm not quite sure what is wrong with Capucine. She has been grouchy of late and I find her a little pale. Nothing I can put my finger on.'

Doctor: 'Bring the child to me immediately. I will squeeze in an emergency appointment.'

With no waiting lists, patients were able to see their GPs on a whim, emerging on a regular basis with shopping bags full of medication. Should fear overcome a patient (an irrational worry that a pimple might be a tumour, or a flutter of the heart a cardiac arrest) anyone in France could bypass their GP completely, and reaching for *Les Pages Jaunes*, take an appointment directly with any number of specialists, from heart surgeons, to gynaecologists, or even brain surgeons. Under the Yellow Pages entry for *Médecins* there were a hundred subcategories through which to browse like a holiday brochure.

As I was currently too sick to stand and hadn't swallowed for hours, I wondered if for extreme cases, like mine, they'd call an ambulance to the château? Or airlift me out?

Bonne-Maman swept back into the kitchen, dressed as always in country tweeds, with a green jacket and skirt, wool tights and sensible shoes. Clearly this part of France was doomed to eternal autumn.

Paying no attention to my dishevelled appearance the lady of the château asked where Yvonne was. I replied that I hadn't seen her and sniffed purposefully.

'She must be occupied with the laundry,' Bonne-Maman replied, 'in which case, you will set the breakfast table. I must wake the children. They always eat before nine.'

'I think I need a doctor *today*,' I replied, realising that with Bonne-Maman a direct approach was best. 'I can't walk.'

Bonne-Maman threw me her quizzical parrot look. 'There is some *paracetamol* in the bathroom. Then some time outdoors with the children in the fresh country air will do you good.'

I dragged myself round the park twice with the children. We were in a hole in the centre of France; the bit you skirted round when on your way to the mountains or the Côte d'Azur; the place where you pulled off at a motorway café to grab a coffee, grabbing your jacket from the backseat as you did so, and commenting that it was much colder in central France, before heading the hell out of there on the *Autoroute du Sud*, towards sandy beaches baking in the sun. It was so cold it felt as if we should be getting our Christmas decorations down from the loft.

The branches of the ancient trees were entwined,

their pale fingers linking above my head to form a thick canopy which was impenetrable to the light. I had borrowed one of Yvonne's jumpers and a waxen hunting coat, which I wore over my summer dress. A pair of oversized wellington boots from the boot cupboard rubbed and tore at my sockless feet. The children amused themselves with sticks and stones. Delphine found a toad. Clémence collected prematurely golden leaves to press in her drawing book. We spotted a squirrel and a hawk and discovered footprints on the wet ground which Baptiste said with certainty must be a deer ... or maybe a badger ... a fox perhaps. By the riverbank we saw willows, with lots of wind, and I wanted to roll in a hole beneath the leaves, and tumble into Ratty's warm nest, or Mole's. I wanted to light a giant fire with a great pile of these mossy twigs which snapped and crackled beneath our boots, and hide in an earthen tunnel beneath the ground. I wanted to hold my feet over an open fire and toast them warm again. I was convinced that in all probability, just like the maid who'd occupied my *chambre de bonne* before me (no doubt buried at the desolate village cemetery before twenty-one of her pale summers had passed), I must have consumption.

By late afternoon the rain was back. We were in the drawing-room playing Scrabble. The fire smoked, and my clothes smelt as if I'd fallen victim to a house fire. I was at a disadvantage as not only was I delirious, but in my current state I could only remember about ten French words. Yvonne took pity on me and brought a hot whisky and lemon. I popped two more paracetamols into the mix. Having been denied food while my cold was starved, I was officially sloshed.

Bonne-Maman was a keen Scrabble player, contesting words and diving for an old dictionary at the slightest altercation, keeping our party waiting for hours as she thumbed through sallow pages. My tiles had formed a word all by themselves: *F-A-N-T-O-M*. Okay, the letters weren't right in either language. But the message was clear. I was not going back to that room again.

'Bonne-Maman,' I said, 'I meant to ask you. Can I change rooms please? I didn't sleep very well.'

'*Et pourquoi pas?*' she demanded. 'Why ever not?'

A glance down at the word on my Scrabble tiles convinced me.

'There's a ghost,' I said, 'that walks round all night and turns the tap on.'

She stared at me a moment, then burst out laughing.

The children looked up in surprise. '*Qu'est-ce-qu'il se passe? Quoi, quoi?*'

Yvonne, hearing the noise, had come into the room and Bonne-Maman quickly translated.

'*Il y a un fantôme dans sa chambre.* She has a ghost in her room!'

They all laughed loudly which hurt my head. The commotion stirred the fire which rose a moment, crackled and roared, before a log shifted, tumbled and fell, extinguishing the flames for good.

With love

CHAPTER 13

Back in Paris, I told Jessica the story.

'Three nights they made me sleep in that room. Same thing every night: footsteps next to my bed; taps gushing on and off. I had to grow hysterical before they'd finally let me change. They think I'm neurotic. Bonne-Maman told Florence I should see a *psychologue*.'

'Ah, *Florence*,' Jessica said, rolling her eyes to the ceiling in the manner one adopts when speaking of a naughty child. 'It's Axel I feel sorry for.'

'Really?' I asked. 'Why?'

I'd forgotten that while I'd been away in that *trou du cul* (arse hole) in central France, Jessica had been caring for my host family.

'Well,' Jessica said conspiratorially, 'while you were away, she was practically never here. Always up at that biscuit factory of hers. Otherwise she was off with Marcel or Hugo – or that Rastafarian drummer.'

'Working on her latest exhibition maybe?'

'Hmmm ...who knows. Anyway, Axel was left to his own devices. I cooked for him most nights. We ate here in the kitchen if he got back late, or in the garden on the nights he came home early. I put a candle in a jar.'

'He came home early! And you *ate* with him?' I couldn't imagine sitting down and eating alone with Axel Blanchard.

As she smiled I noticed for the first time that her alabaster skin had warmed a degree in my absence. While I'd been condemned to the Underworld with Orpheus in the land of eternal autumn, Jessica had been sunbathing! Her skin was still white of course, her trademark foundation blotting out her every spot and freckle, but there was an unmistakeable glow to her cheeks. She'd clearly been making use of the Blanchard's washing machine, as much for herself as the family, wearing a crisp andclean-looking cotton dress. She had bought a new pair of T-strap sandals too.

She leant towards me in the way I remembered from school: secrets and sometimes lies, but told so convincingly, I was never quite sure.

'There was a *bit* of an incident,' she said. 'I'd done my jobs and gone for a lie down with my book. D.H. Lawrence, rather whimsical after Beckett, I know. Anyway, *it's been a while, you know*,' she stared at me with a meaningful gaze, 'so I thought I'd *pleasure* myself. Sun through the windows, feeling sensual. You know how it goes after a bit of *Lady Chatterley*. So, there I was, lost to the world, when I heard a noise. I looked up and who should I see, but *him*.'

Oh god, let her not say his name. How was I ever going to

iron those underpants with a straight face again? A dramatic pause and then she said it.

'Monsieur Blanchard! Watching me.'

'For fuck's sake, Jessica! What did he say?'

'Nothing, he gave *that* smile. You know, the boyish one, where his teeth suddenly look too big for his mouth.'

'*Then* what?'

'He left. Thought things might have felt awkward afterwards, but far from it. He's a man of the world our Axel.'

Jessica had begun painting the studio as promised. A trail of stiff, dried-up brushes and congealed paint cans were strewn on the floor of her studio. The walls were a dainty lemon colour now, the bed pushed back to one wall, a stepladder in the middle, the old 1920s marble fireplace splattered with specks of paint. She'd been wearing one of those blue zip-up suits workmen wear. She climbed into it like a tent, so it covered her cotton dress from top to bottom. Her hair was clipped back, and she looked like one of those fresh-faced girls from a paint advertisement. I felt a pang of sadness imagining how it would have been if David and I had been decorating our first Parisian flat, making love on an old leather sofa in the corner before the undercoat was even dry. Jessica's bed was covered with books and papers, notepads filled with the pages of her novel. She looked quite settled. I wondered how long they'd let her stay – maybe Monsieur Blanchard *did* like her, and Florence was too busy with her moody artist friends to even notice. All the same, when next I saw Florence I was quite alarmed when she asked with a serious look if we could have a little word. In private.

Florence instructed me to make some tea and to meet her in the garden – more than just a quick word then? We sat at a little green wrought-iron table on which there was a jam-jar with a burnt-down candle on the inside, and with a great splodge of melted wax congealed at the bottom. So, Jessica *had* been having candlelit suppers in the garden with Monsieur Blanchard after all.

At first, we chatted about Château de Trémouillet and my trip away with Bonne-Maman. Florence smiled wistfully and said that she understood I had not had a pleasant trip, what with the flu, the ghosts and the terrible rain.

'It always rains in Trémouillet,' she said. 'I can never quite bring myself to go.' I knew how she felt which emboldened me to say: 'I hope I never have to see that place again as long as I live. I'd rather leave and find a new job.'

Her head twitched upright, as she adopted Bonne-Maman's own bird-like gaze. I'd noticed that Florence could quickly snap out of her artistic and melancholic mood if her domestic comforts were in any way threatened.

'But you will not leave us?' she asked. 'We have grown so fond of you.'

'No, no,' I said quickly, realising in panic that I'd better not be too hasty because I hadn't anywhere *to* go. My bedroom at home had been given to my younger brother Steven, and his room had been turned into what my mother now referred to as the 'ironing room.' As if to make certain I would never return, they had sold the single bed that was once there. My mother had grown used to my absence in the last three years and my father, I knew, was planning a new life once my brother left for uni. Gran was dead and Grandad's nerves would never have coped with a lodger. Nobody wanted me. My salary as a *jeune fille au pair* was so low it would be impossible to save up for a deposit on a flat. The Blanchards were all I had.

Florence sighed and sipped her tea.

'There is a little matter I wanted to discuss,' she said, 'concerning your friend Jessica.'

I spluttered on my drink and the next few minutes were taken up wiping my mouth and taking a second calmer sip. But Florence had not forgotten her line of thought.

'It seems to me that *Jessica* (she says it in that lovely French way JESS-I-CA) may have feelings towards my husband. I watched her closely while you were away.'

'Oh god, I'm so sorry. Do you want me to ask her to leave?'

Florence smiled and poured more tea.

'*Mais non, mais non,*' she said, 'of course not. May I be frank with you?"

'Err, yes, of course. Please.'

'For you to understand, I will tell you a story. Let us say it is a story about people you do not know, for I do not wish you to feel uncomfortable.'

'Okaaay ...'

'Many years ago, there was a young nineteen-year-old girl who had not yet made love. She dreamt of travelling the world, but she came from a very sheltered background where an adventurous and unconventional life seemed impossible. Her family were strict; old school; Catholic. Her school holidays were spent, well – shall we say in a very *rainy* place with bats and flies. She had not known what it was to fall in love. She met a charming boy: blonde, serious, hardworking and good-looking. He was from fine stock – Catholic also. Both families were very pleased, and soon they were married, and one after the other, three beautiful children were born. There was nothing that the young girl could complain about. *Vous me comprenez bien?*'

I did. Axel was the perfect father providing for his family and making a splash on Parisian posters.

'But this young girl she dreamt of other things, which were not so material. She wanted to create things with her hands, beautiful things that the world would remember. She learnt later on, as you will learn, that there are different kinds of love.'

This was a surprising thought. I had only until that time considered one type of love. Florence, in her fervour, had forgotten the fictitious characters in her earlier story.

'My husband, may I be honest with you, has only slept with one woman and that woman is me.'

'Isn't that a good thing?'

'It is a beautiful idea, but we all grow, *n'est-ce pas?* Once he came home so angry, *mon pauvre chéri*. He'd been away on a business trip and his secretary had let herself into his room. He found her lying naked on his bed. Axel was furious. He threw her out and came home to tell me immediately as if he had somehow done something wrong. *La pauvre fille.* I felt so sorry for her. He was harsh. It took *courage* of a sort to do what she did. She must have been desperate. I told my husband maybe, just this once, he should have said yes.'

The idea of husband-sharing appalled me. 'But why? It shows he loves you, doesn't it?'

'Yes, of course, but it is only one *kind* of love. There are many types you know. There is the one we recognize in our moments of greatest passion – the one we most often experience at the *beginning* of a relationship; though this type of love cannot last forever and so we seek it again. But I see that I am confusing you.'

'I don't see why you would want him to cheat on you.'

'Last year,' she continued, 'I was reading through some of my old diaries. I was reading memories of a very special day in my life when I was already married. A day filled with experiences which – religiously and morally speaking – some would say life should no longer have reserved for me. If you follow my meaning. But a day which I would not have renounced for all the world either. Well, I discovered that Axel had found this entry, and had also written on this private page. He had made a comment in pencil just above mine, where the words nestled so many years waiting for me to find them: *So now, Florence, I know where you were.* He had known all that time of this afternoon of pleasure, yet he had never said a word!'

'You were with another man? Is that why you didn't

mind about the secretary on his bed?'

Florence smiled.

'May I speak plainly? If your friend Jessica wants to sleep with my husband, it is not from me that she will receive an objection. *Au contraire.* But he will not leave his children or his wife for her. She should know this from the start.'

The concept of *not* being jealous was alien to me. I'd once had a jealous fit over Steve lusting after a woman on a frozen peas advert. The idea of David making love with another woman had made me sick with jealousy. My mother had taken my father back after an affair and to mark the occasion he had bought her a new wedding ring. It would not have been enough for me. It was a symbolic act. My mother had had a few of her own, including cutting up his clothes on the front lawn, smashing the windows, and hiding a rusty screw in his mashed potatoes. I couldn't imagine my mother inscribing my father's diary with such a neat little phrase – his car maybe.

Not only was Florence unfaithful, but she was prepared to love her husband even if he were to sleep with Jessica. And even more intriguing than *this*, was Axel's self-control, and his own ability to hold on secretly to the knowledge that his wife had cheated on him. When he had written in her diary, he must have known that one day it would be discovered, but he had no means of knowing how many years the message would lie there waiting for her. Perhaps Florence wasn't the sort to read over past entries, scooting through her year and filling each blank page with her careful French print. It was possible that after her death, her children would have been the first to read their father's words; while Axel continued the treadmill of his grey-suited existence, coming home each night to eat with his wife while their children were in bed, visiting the theatre or the opera house once a month, biting down all those feelings of anger, upset and jealousy – for surely, he must have endured these.

From then on, I ironed Axel's shirts in reverence. The man was a martyr. I wasn't sure that sleeping with Jessica would be his salvation. This was the same girl who had declared undying love for our headmaster only three years before, causing untold scandal in our comprehensive school.

Despite this, I informed Jessica that Florence had effectively left the path to Monsieur Blanchard's arms clear. Jessica said she'd bear it in mind, but that she wanted more for herself than to be a French mistress. She wasn't interested in a *cinq à sept*, as the French referred to an affair; thus called because of the time slot during which such assignations usually took place. It was Florence's certainty that her couple would never split that put a dampener on things. I imagined Jessica quite liked the idea of being the female figure in the backdrop of the next Axel Blanchard poster; sending the children off to boarding school *poste haste* ('first thing I'd do', she said), with Florence conveniently ensconced in her newly renovated biscuit factory, sculpting her phallic symbols.

Once Jessica realised that she was not about to be upgraded from garden cottage to eastern wing, the idea lost some of its appeal. As she said, it was a bit rich Florence giving her permission to become her own husband's plaything. Affairs were meant to be moments of heightened irresistible illicit passion, weren't they? Not organised over tea by the wife and her nanny.

I never discovered what Monsieur Blanchard might or might not have seen Jessica doing that day at the cottage. Whenever I asked Jessica, she gave me her secretive smile.

Shortly afterwards Jessica and I saw a film that came to symbolise our every literary and romantic ideal, re-affirming our life goals and heightening the sense that somehow, somewhere, we would find the true purpose to our lives. It accelerated the end of our *au pair* days much faster than expected.

The Dead Poet's Society had aired in Paris earlier that year. Jessica and I saw it on the Champs Elysées one night after a day spent walking around the city, our pockets empty, longing to pop into one of the golden brasseries or tearooms, but with barely five francs between us.

It was a Sunday: our day of rest. Though the rest of Jessica's week could hardly be called strenuous. It was our Sunday routine to have lunch in Paris (money providing) and then to wander round the museums, buying arty postcards for friends back home, or to stick on our bedroom walls. We would visit Le Louvre, Le Musée Rodin, or my favourite, the old converted train station Le Musée d'Orsay; our usual ports of call on those halcyon days free from the children.

By late afternoon, we were ready for coffee on the Boulevard de Saint Michel, perusing the paperbacks bought from Gibert Jeune in Saint Germain or WH Smith's on the rue de Rivoli. Our only news of home came via the newspapers, which were hard to get hold of. Smith's sold newspapers, magazines and books in English, and the newsagents at the Gare Saint Lazare stocked copies of *The Daily Mail* with its usual dramas one day removed from our French lives. Everything else was in French. We relished anything we could find in English in the days before illegal Sky boxes and satellite TV would beam out the BBC to British expats, as we suffered dubbed repeats of *Dallas* or *Little House on the Prairie* or plodded our way through French newspapers. Each week we picked up a copy of the *Pariscope* from one of the kiosks outside the Gare Saint Lazare; a small, pocket-sized journal which listed the films showing in original version across the city. This is how we first heard of *The Dead Poet's Society*.

After our first viewing Jessica and I met back in the Hessian Sack. She wouldn't let me in the cottage as she said she hadn't washed up for a few days. I lit a candle and we sat in silence a moment, both aware that something important had taken place. My skin still felt grubby from the metro, my fingers sticky from the fish-burger I'd eaten at McDonald's, but my heart was singing. It was a sad film, but it was also a film which celebrated literature and poetry. It was a film that introduced the concept of *carpe diem* – seize the day.

'What the fuck are we doing skivvying for the Blanchards?' Jessica asked.

It seemed churlish to point out that I was doing most of the skivvying, so I lit another candle instead. We'd filched some empty jam jars from the kitchen for the occasion.

'We have to get out,' she said, looking at me intently. 'We have to run away, live a life of adventure, find love all of this! Life is slipping between our fingers while I dead-head roses and you fold undies.'

I nodded solemnly. Until that moment I hadn't seriously considered leaving the safety of the Blanchards' home and stepping out alone into the big city. I hadn't even started my French course.

'We need jobs,' I said.

'In theatre,' Jessica replied randomly, reclining on my bed. 'I'm going to ring round tomorrow. They must have roles for two English girls.'

I was doubtful but clung to two magic words. *Carpe diem*. Why not? Someone had to work on stage. Why not us? Okay, we couldn't speak French, but I'd studied drama in my first year at university and had been awarded a First for a production plan of Ibsen's *The Doll's House*. Nothing was impossible, was it?

'And you need a lover,' Jessica said. 'I've been talking to Delphine and she reckons her mother is jealous of you and Marcel.'

'You've been talking to Delphine! That's ridiculous. There's nothing between us, even if I wanted something. Though I admit, I like him.'

'I don't believe you. Come on, tell me.'

'Well, he did come down to the cellar and kiss me, but only the once. And before we left for that bloody awful château, he invited me for a drink … I think.'

'Where?'

'On the roof top of La Samaritaine. The department store.'

She was impressed now, telling me that it was only one of the most romantic roof-top terraces in the city.

'And you didn't go?'

'I couldn't. I was stuffed into Bonne-Maman's car and driven to the country to pick up dead flies.'

'More skivvying! You see? This is what I mean. Fate throws opportunity at us, and we are helpless to accept. All because we are in service.'

'Jane Eyre was in service.'

'She got out. Anyway, back to Marcel. You must tell him your feelings. Send him a card.'

'I can't! I don't know his address.'

'Delphine does. Well, she knows where her mother's address book is.'

'I wouldn't dare.'

'Humph, and you say that after what we've seen *tonight.* – Seize the day! Tell him. Write down on a piece of paper what you want to say.' She hurled a biro at me from my bag which sprawled open on the bed. Reluctantly I unpinned one of Clémence's drawings from the back of my door and scribbled down my first thoughts. 'Go on then, read it.'

Dear Marcel,
You seem a very nice man. The first time we met you made

me laugh when you sucked your green beans in the side of your
mouth. I would like to hear you play the piano one day, if ever
you invite me to your flat, and drink tea with you before that
on the roof top of La Samaritaine. (If you still want to).
Karen

I handed the paper to Jessica, who read it aloud, a crease forming between her eyebrows. She crumpled it up.

'That's crap. You sound about ten. Write something a bit feisty. Pithy.'

I was too tired to be pithy and reached for my dictionary which had a middle section of pink-paged quotations. It didn't take long before I spotted a familiar word, almost the same in both languages: architect.

Chacun est l'architecte de sa vie. The architect of one's own life, is oneself. Or something like that. Perfect! Marcel would appreciate the cryptic intelligence of my words. As our old headmaster had said, brevity is all.

Jessica was satisfied, saying it left enough to the imagination and was subtler than talk of green beans. It was decided. The next day I'd find a suitable card and send it to Marcel, unsigned.

CHAPTER 14

In the days that followed the posting of the card – the black-and-white Doisneau photograph of a couple kissing – I reached a state of frenzy. Was it my imagination, or was Florence pounding her crutches harder on the parquet floors? When she paid me my weekly wage she was no longer warm or chatty and didn't invite me for tea, or say goodbye when she slammed the door for her drumming lesson.

'Jealous,' Jessica said. 'It's obvious. He's told her.

Green-eyed monster.'

Quotes from *Othello* still peppered our dialogue; remnants of sixth form.

'But why would she be jealous? She wasn't jealous of her own husband, so why Marcel? I mean he's not *her* lover, is he?'

Jessica raised her eyebrows.

'Oh dear,' she sighed. 'You've a lot to learn.' 'No! He *can't* be.'

'Trust me. Delphine more or less told me.' 'You're lying.'

'Alright, maybe. She told me her mother was *very* close to Marcel. Very *protective* of him. She suspects the worst and wants you out.'

'I wish you wouldn't do that! I never know what's true with you: like that story about you masturbating and Axel watching.'

'Ah, Axel ...'

She smiled and lay back on the bed, crushing my *carte orange*.

Jessica's comments unsettled me so much, that the next time Marcel came to lunch I was in a complete panic; all fingers and thumbs with the serving bowls, and with a face as red as a baboon's bottom. Marcel smiled at me and raised his eyebrows. I didn't dare look in his direction. Florence allowed me to serve the lunch, but I could see from the number of places set that I was not invited. Broody Hugo was back, foul-tempered as always. He didn't know, or care, what was going on, I was sure. I hovered in the kitchen knowing I was meant to serve dessert. Marcel stood up and brought out a jug for more water. I dropped it. Florence was cross. I was sent to iron.

Now that Florence knew I'd sent the card – I *knew* that she knew; her whole attitude towards me had changed – I needed to seek new employment. Jessica was right. Our days were numbered. I needed to run before she threw me out. Jessica said girls who ran were called *bolters*. Doing a runner was a concept she'd picked up from Nancy Mitford novels, and henceforth this was our code name: The Bolters.

To make matters worse, having now thrown myself at the mercy of The Universe, and having grabbed it by both hands and squeezed it hard, Marcel hadn't called. Or at least no-one had told me if he had. He was no doubt laughing at the silly English au-pair girl and her crush. How old must he be? Forty maybe? Older? It was hard to tell. I was only twenty-one – he must have thought I was as immature as one of the kids. What was I thinking? That bloody film was to blame! 'O captain, My Captain!' And what right had Florence to be jealous of Marcel anyway? She should be jealous of Jessica's candlelit suppers with her husband, but no! Jessica got off scot-free, with green lights all round, practically lighting the corridor to the eastern wing bedroom like a flight path at Heathrow, while *I* got the cold shoulder.

Jessica said we needed a night out. I'd been paid by a poker-faced Florence, and as in days gone by, my friend had honed in on the franc notes burning a hole in my pocket. The deal with Jessica was that she wasn't paid by the Blanchards but given the garden cottage in lieu of work. After that first breakfast, the Blanchards didn't appear to have considered how or where she ate, failing to notice that I often cooked an extra portion, or that down in the cellar Mr Blanchard's dusty wine collection was dwindling and that his whisky bottles were topped up with water.

We found a Chinese restaurant on the square at the end of our street, squeezed in between a BNP bank and a *boulangerie*. Its main draw was the cheap 50-franc all-inclusive menu advertised on a glitzy board outside.

The restaurant was packed and decorated with the usual golden dragons and red fans. On the wall, there was an electronic montage of a waterfall, in which the water miraculously fell over a 3D rock, and a flock of blue birds soared over a multi-coloured rainbow. As we walked into the foyer, we rubbed the stomach of a fat red Buddha for luck.

The owners ran the restaurant by themselves. A smiling, nodding couple, they ushered us in like royalty. The man, who was shorter than me, wore boots with prominent heels which clicked on the laminate floor as he walked. His wife, dressed in a tight silk dress, was heavily pregnant. The man showed us to a corner table next to a statue of a golden cat with a waving arm.

'Let's hope she doesn't drop while we're here,' Jessica whispered. I knew nothing could come between my friend and her food. Least of all a birthing mother.

It was no more expensive than McDonald's and a lot tastier. The menu included a bowl of spicy soup, two spring rolls, a helping of prawn curry and a bowl of rice. For dessert, there was a choice between a rock-hard biscuit studded with sesame seeds, or a small helping of tinned lychees. To accompany the meal there was a choice of either a Chinese beer or a small *pichet* of red wine. We took the wine. Other than a change in menu, there was a purpose to our meeting outside of the house. Jessica had a plan and told me that our days in service were over. The Bolters were about to do what they did best.

I thought back with a shudder to an incident of humiliation which had occurred earlier that afternoon, as the two of us sat at the bottom of the Blanchard staircase, phone in hand. Using the Minitel (a small machine which was an effective precursor of the Internet, and conveniently listed the name, number and address of any establishment in France) Jessica had sourced the number of the Opéra Garnier in Paris. Florence was at the doctor's and the children were upstairs playing cards. Jessica insisted that I was to make the call and offer our services on stage (no less) at the opera house.

'We can't sing.'

Jessica waved away my objection with a flick of her wrist. 'They'll want people of all sorts. Extras and stuff, you'll see.'

'You ring then?'

'No, your phone French is better than mine.' 'No, it isn't.'

'Do you want to spend the rest of your life skivvying?' I was about to be massacred – and we both knew it. '*Avez-vous du travail pour deux anglaises?*' I asked with-out preamble. (Do you have work for two English girls?) Stunned silence.

'*Quoi?*' The disgust was tangible in the woman's voice. '*Avez-vous du travail pour deux actrices anglaises ?*'

The addition of the word 'actresses' was optimistic. Jessica had once been turned down for the role of Viola in the school production of *Twelfth Night* and my parents had refused to let me audition at all, on account of having to be allowed out of the bungalow at night for rehearsals.

'Non.'

'Vous êtes sûr ?'

'*Certain.*' The woman growled and hung up thus ending our careers in the Paris opera house before they had begun.

At dinner, I was nervous at any further mention of escape plans.

'I have the solution,' Jessica said, producing a rolled-up magazine from her bag and placing it on the restaurant table. 'Here lies the answer to our problems.'

The magazine was called the *Le PAP* – or *Le Particulier à Particulier* – a sizeable wedge of a journal advertising hundreds and thousands of houses or flats up and down the country that were for sale or rent. There was an entire middle section on Paris which was divided into *arrondissements* or districts. Naturally our favourite arrondissement was the 18th – which housed the Sacre Coeur and La Place du Tertre in Montmartre.

Jessica had first shared her vision of her Parisian apartment with me way back in sixth form. The stage set to any arts film based in Paris always resembled Montmartre in our minds, and Jessica's studio flat was to be located on a cobbled street just off the Place du Tertre, a top-floor apartment under slate rooftops, dotted with fat cooing pigeons. Below there would be a bar (we now knew this was Jacques' bar Le Tartempion) for late-night drinks and *tartare de boeuf* to ward off anaemia. Consumption had been eradicated from Paris by the late eighties, to the chagrin of my friend. Nothing would have set off her bohemian image as a writer as much as a good bout of TB. Anaemia would have to do. In this loft apartment, Jessica would write her novel, bashing it out on her old Remington portable, shipped out from England. I'd heard the story many times, but after two glasses of acidic, screwtop wine, I was beginning to believe the dream might come true

I turned to the section marked *Paris 18ème*. Jessica had brought her lucky pen and we circled the most interesting adverts, concentrating on two-bedroom flats with a separate sitting room. It was clear from the price of rentals that a month working for the Blanchards would barely cover a week in a one-bedroom studio flat, but the magic of *The Dead Poet's Society* lingered. If you wanted something badly enough, The Universe would send it to you.

Jessica had all the answers. We would look for jobs temping in the business centre of La Défense – well-paid bilingual positions during which time we could work on our language skills. Once we had secured employment, we would sign a rental contract on a flat the same week, vacating the Blanchard household on the day we started work. I wondered how Florence would cope with school looming on the horizon, if Jessica and I bolted, but I didn't voice my fears. I predicted my friend's response: 'Her look out – not ours. She'll find some other poor sod.'

By the time the silver bowl of lychees arrived, we had scored most of the pages in the journal. We were the last customers in the restaurant, Jessica claiming you should always get your money's worth. The pregnant woman had bid us goodnight, leaving her husband to attend to our needs. As if in response to her thoughts, the owner tiptapped his way to our table bringing over a saucer laden with sesame cakes.

'*Cadeau de la maison,*' he said. 'On the house.'

'*Merci,*' Jessica replied, slotting the biro behind her ear and taking a bite. '*Très généreux de votre part.*'

The man hovered a moment and leaning over the table, looked at the journal spread out between us.

'You look for place to live,' he ventured in English, with a heavy Chinese accent.

'Yes,' Jessica said, her lips thick with crumbs from the sesame-seed cakes. 'We'll be starting work in Paris soon and are looking for a place in the centre. *Paris 18ème,* no doubt. Somewhere near the Lapin Agile.' She picked up her glass and tilted it, fully aware that it was empty.

'Nice cakes,' she said, swallowing down one last hard morsel. 'A little *dry* perhaps?'

The man scuttled off, his feet clipping the floor. He returned almost immediately with a full pitcher of red wine.

'Again, on the house,' he said.

How generous he was! If he was this kind to *all* his customers, there wouldn't be much room for profit. After all, we had only paid 100 francs between us (the equivalent of about £10 or less) and we'd been ensconced there for at least two hours.

The man poured us each a full glass. It was a different *cru* from the first bottle, full-bodied and fruity, leaving our tongues the colour of bilberries. My head was swimming and as I stared at the picture of the moving waterfall, and listened to the jangling music on a loop, I started to feel hypnotised. Jessica, who hadn't spent the whole day ironing, and cleaning the children's bedrooms, was wide awake and quickly fell into a serious sounding discussion with the man. I caught the tail end of what they were saying.

'My cousin very serious *agent immobilier*. Good realtor. Do you good deal as customers of mine.'

While I had been sailing beneath a Canton sky filled with blue birds, Jessica had written down a name and an address of a real estate agency on a red paper napkin and set up an appointment for the next day.

'Ten o'clock tomorrow,' the man said and clicked away.

'We don't have any money,' I pointed out. 'Why bother?'

She shrugged. 'I explained that. Anyway, he says we can sort it out later.'

'Sort what out later?' 'The rent, silly.'

'Are you *sure*?'

'Course I'm sure. We ASKED and we have RECEIVED. When you start to live your life by celestial rules, wondrous things can happen. And this is just the beginning!'

Next morning, I met Jessica at the garden cottage at nine o'clock sharp. We wanted to make a quick getaway. My household duties didn't officially start until 2 pm, but if Florence saw me she might ask me to sort out the odd-sock basket or something, my presence a dangerous reminder of a hundred jobs that needed doing.

Thoughts of a romantic Parisian flat had kept me awake all night. It seemed incredible to think that somehow there could be a solution to our problems without a deposit or a salary. But then the Chinese restaurant owner, with his pregnant wife, seemed to be a steady family sort. It was clear he'd taken one look at us and seen that we were the genuine scholarly type. The Universe had stepped in to help us. Jessica was right. It had guided us to the restaurant and granted our wishes. It had convinced the restaurant owner that he should give us a chance. Our Faith had been repaid. It was Universal Law in all its splendour!

I found Jessica dressed in a tight black skirt and an off-white blouse, which looked suspiciously like her old school uniform shirt. She was wearing high-heel shoes that I'd not seen before (I had an awful feeling they might be Florence's from her pre-hippy, pre-drumming days) and had morphed into a pretty good copy of Ian Fleming's Miss Moneypenny with a pair of thick black glasses on her nose, picked up from Oxfam. She didn't need glasses but liked to dress the part and had a vast array of accoutrements to hand for most occasions.

'I want a serious bilingual assistant look.' she said. 'Got to make sure there's nothing of the nanny about me. No egg on the collar.'

'It's been awhile since there's been any egg on your collar.'

'Metaphorically speaking. Anyway, I've been in close contact with you, and before I know it, it'll be flat shoes and flared skirts and my biorhythms all set in time to the nursery clock.'

She was right of course. I was starting to know without looking at my watch that it was time for *le goûter*.

I felt differently today. Knowing as I did that the end was nigh, the house had taken on the air of a hotel room on the last morning of a vacation. I absorbed its familiar objects: the pea-green kitchen, the wooden phallus, The Submarine, wondering if I would ever see them again. Thoughts of my departure were tinged with sadness, as I imagined dragging my case down the stairs for the last time and out of the front door to face the unknown. Part of me wanted to stay in the Hessian Sack; part of me wanted to escape to Paris to the life that was waiting. There'd been a lot of upheaval in the last few months; a lot of goodbyes. There was something to be said for staying home safe and pretending to be one of the children. But life was calling.

Marcel on the other hand, most definitely hadn't, though he must have received my declaration of love days ago. Now I knew his address in the Bastille perhaps I could go there one morning and accidentally bump into him on his morning trip to the baker's for croissants. He might invite me to the roof-top terrace of La Samaritaine again. We arrived at the estate agency just before ten. It was in the north of Paris, at the Porte de Pantin. Our journey involved a trip through the bustling Gare du Nord which felt more like Ghana than a Parisian metro station. It was packed with commuters in bright robes and itinerant salesmen with rugs spread out displaying their wares. In the station, there was a vegetable stall set out with rows of bright bananas and papayas, the air tinged with the scent of urine. No-one seemed to mind trading in the bowels of the earth.

A stallholder cackled with customers and tossed a bunch of speckled bananas into a wafer-thin plastic bag.

The exit to the Porte de Pantin metro led up to the Boulevard Jean Jaurès. We asked for directions and found the agency some minutes' walk behind the park and down a narrow side street where there were few other shops. The shop window was Parisian chic, in contemporary steel and glass. In the window there was a neat display of about twenty rental flats, all of which were beyond our means. I nudged Jessica.

'We can't afford this, look! You must be mad. Are you sure that Chinese man fully understood our situation? What did you tell him exactly?'

She didn't answer. I knew she didn't want the dream to end.

'*Carpe diem,*' she said, and marched into the shop.

Two young men were seated at an office desk. On the side reserved for employees, a young Chinese man with black round-rimmed glasses was busy filling in a form. On the other side a smartly dressed man glanced at his watch and sighed impatiently. The men barely acknowledged us as we entered. The agent brandished a sheet of paper, which looked like a contract, in the air. Proud of his work. He handed it to the customer, and watched as the man signed the bottom of each page with a flourish of his fountain pen.

Jessica, never one to wait in line, had begun to fidget noticeably and cleared her throat loudly. Just then the door opened with a jangle and a man in black heels with boots tip-tapped in – our friend from the Chinese restaurant. He observed the younger man busy at work, and fired off a stream of Chinese as authoritative as a round of gun shots. The younger man threw his pen down onto the desk, raised his arms in the air and retaliated. The conversation continued for a few moments, with our friend waving his arms and pointing at us, and the other man waving his arms and pointing at his client. Finally, the agent pushed his chair back and grabbed the contract back from the customer's hand. The Frenchman was clearly not impressed.

'*Que se passe-t-il?*' he demanded.

The agent shook his head and looked as if he might spit. '*Je suis désolé*. My apologies. The flat is already let. We appear to have wasted your time.'

'Let, to whom?' the man asked. 'It wasn't let a minute ago, when you dragged me out of a meeting to get me here.'

The agent pointed to us, the sorry culprits.

'The flat is let to these two girls,' he said dolefully. 'I'm sorry. I can show you a nice little *deux pièces* on the other side of La Villette if you will allow me.'

The customer scraped his chair back roughly on the polished parquet.

'There will be no more *rendez-vous*!' he said, grabbing his briefcase. As he reached the door he turned to face us. 'I hope you are satisfied,' he added in English. 'For one month I had this flat reserved and now, suddenly, *mystérieusement*, it is no longer available. *C'est inadmissible!* He slammed the door in fury and headed out into the morning sun.

Our man was all apologies, begging us to sit down and drink a glass of water. The estate agent didn't look pleased. He tore a fresh form from his pad and turned to face us.

'We will speak in English,' he said, more as a statement of fact than a question. 'We need to take some basic details before showing you the property. Full names?'

The first question wasn't hard. Date of birth, neither. When it came to the part about our current address, Jessica leant forwards and said in her snooty Margaret Thatcher voice, that we did not wish any letters to be sent to our current abode, thank you very much. The last thing we needed was for Florence to see a contract from an estate agency. Frowning, the man crossed out this section and wrote *étrangères* in large letters. The man's final question threw us both. Even Mrs Thatcher had the grace to look embarrassed.

'Name of your current employer and net amount of your monthly salary.'

Luckily our friend from the restaurant was quick to step in. He said something in Chinese to the young man who raised a pair of neatly plucked brows in return. The agent returned to his form and crossed out the remaining sections at the bottom of the page.

I was beginning to think of our Chinese friend as being a kind of Magwitch figure from *Great Expectations*: the escaped convict who set up a trust for the unwitting protagonist Pip; the mysterious benefactor who worked tirelessly behind the scenes to ensure that Pip had

everything he would need in life. *Our* benefactor was
a small man in high-heeled boots. It was nice to have a
benefactor, though why this man had chosen to bestow
such kindness on two girls who had eaten just once in
his restaurant, and picked the cheapest meals possible,
eating all the complimentary prawn crackers we could
lay our hands on and holding out our bowls for more, I
couldn't imagine. I could only assume that it was because
we were all foreigners together. Florence had told me
how racist the French could be to her African friends;
and how Fuschia had found it impossible to find a job
coming as she did from Gabon. Surely it must be the
same with the Chinese man too. Perhaps he felt for us
and wanted to reach out and help us take those first steps
to independence. He had nothing to worry about of
course. If he would allow us the first month rent-free, as
Jessica claimed, then we would easily find work, even if it
was in a bar or a supermarket, to pay him back. Perhaps
we could pay a bit extra to make up for his kindness.

The agent opened a drawer and took out a set of keys.
Then he wrote down a number on a slip of paper. The
door code.

'I will do the viewing myself,' our benefactor said,
picking up the keys. Whatever the relationship between
the two men was, there was no doubt that our man was
in control. The agent showed little resistance. We filed
out of the shop. It occurred to me that I still didn't know
our benefactor's real name, though we were following
him to a viewing of a place that could potentially be
ours. It seemed awkward to start introducing ourselves

at this stage of the game.

We followed the road back the way we had come, to the rue Eugène Jumin, which was on the road behind the metro station. N° 27 was a grand five-floor Haussmannian block with a sandy brick facade. Magwitch keyed in the digicode and we followed him up five flights to the top, his little boots tapping the wooden stairs all the way. He opened the door to reveal a spacious and sunny studio apartment, with two windows facing out towards Le Parc de la Villette. Although the balcony wasn't big enough to sit on, there were two wrought-iron railings with plenty of space for flowers. My mind's eye busied itself at once, filling the space with crimson geraniums in terracotta pots. The middle section of the room was divided in two by a kitchen counter which stood proud like a bar. Behind it there was space for an oven and a sink. Beyond the kitchen area, there was a door to a compact bathroom with a shower and toilet. Hopes for a bedroom each and a sitting room to boot were dashed, but penniless and jobless as we were, if we could secure this place, it would be nothing short of a miracle. Magwitch dangled the keys tantalisingly before our eyes.

'Well, what you think? Okay, yes? You want it or no?'

We agreed that it was more than okay and that we would like to move in the following weekend. There wasn't a stick of furniture in there, but Magwitch asked no questions on this front and we told no lies. We would need to send another request to The Universe for a sofa and two beds, not to mention some kitchen appliances, but for now I was happy to have four walls we could call our own.

Magwitch invited us back to the office and demanded coffee from the man at the desk. Once served, the agent settled down at his desk, and produced a blank contract to be signed, which Magwitch explained was a three-year lease. When I came to the section marked DEPOSIT I hesitated. Once again there was a brief exchange in Chinese. Magwitch took the paper from me and wrote 9,000 francs in his neat hand. I protested.

'*Non, non, vous ne comprenez pas.* We have no money.' The man was asking us for an impossible sum. Florence currently paid me 1,800 francs a month (about £180 pounds), which was the going rate for an au pair since there were no outgoings for food and rent etc. The agent was asking for a deposit five times this amount. Magwitch smiled reassuringly and took a fat brown envelope from the breast pocket of his jacket. He opened it and fanned out a spread of notes on the table as if we were at a casino. The agent gathered up the notes and put them inside his desk drawer.

'Soon you will have jobs,' Magwitch said, seeing my look of alarm, 'and then you will pay us back. This is how it works in our community. I place my trust in you today, when you have nothing. I help you when you are in the gutter. Later, there is payback. The system cannot fail – and if it does,' he giggled suddenly, like a small rotund dwarf, 'well, people who cheat us, they find the world is a bad place.'

He placed a hand clad with golden rings before his mouth as if about to cough and I noticed that he had tucked his inner finger inside, holding it close to his palm so that it looked as if he had lost his middle digit. Jessica nudged me to make sure I'd seen. Magwitch rubbed his nose and laughed. Then he stood, shook both our hands and handed over the set of keys from his back pocket. The keys were still warm, a reminder of Magwitch's vital presence in the whole affair.

'Goodbye for now,' he called, and scurried off.

CHAPTER 15

'That was a breeze,' I said, dragging Jessica onto a café terrace next door for *un grand café crème*. Jessica was quiet but determined.

'Did you see that whole finger business?' she demanded.

'Yes, bit weird wasn't it. At first, I thought he'd lost one in a meat-slicer or something. Then I saw it was tucked behind his palm. Like a secret code. You know … *The Man in The Brown Suit*, that kind of thing.'

'You don't get it, do you?'

'Get what?'

'It *was* a code. To say they'll chop our fingers off if we don't pay. They're Mafia.'

'Don't be daft – the Mafia are Italian, aren't they?'

'Not if they're in some sort of a Triad, or whatever it's called, you know, the *Chinese* Mafia,' Jessica said knowingly.

It took four *cafés crème* and as many croissants to talk this through. By now my wages had been spent with only a few francs remaining in my purse, but for once Jessica produced a tightly folded note from somewhere in the cavernous folds of her bag. It was important to discuss this before we returned home. The silver keys to the apartment lay on the table between us, the promise of a brighter future.

'Shall we take them back?' I asked.

We were both silent. I was sure Jessica was remembering the flat with as much excitement as I was. The uninterrupted view over the rooftops to La Villette; the jazz concerts she'd told me they held live in the park each year. I visualised the windows open, the music wafting over the geraniums and the two of us sitting down around the table with dinner guests. Marcel perhaps. We'd have a yellow gingham tablecloth and a jar of white tulips from a local market. We didn't have a table or a vase – these were irksome details – but Jessica, as if reading my thoughts, reassured me that soon we would both be working in La Défense business centre, dressed to the nines in a slick office, and with plenty of cash for furnishings.

'My French is too bad to be bilingual,' I pointed out. 'And so is yours.'

She glared at me. 'So, give the keys back.' We ordered a third coffee to share.

'What's the worst that can happen?' Jessica asked, licking her finger and dabbing croissant crumbs from her plate.

'They cut our fingers off.' 'But in what circumstances?'

'If we don't pay our rent. That's what he said, right? Though we would pay, wouldn't we?' I asked this question quite slowly and deliberately. It wasn't often that Jessica's purse saw the light of day, and I wasn't taking any chances.

'*Obviously* we'll pay,' she said, closing her bag. 'So, what are the other risks?'

We couldn't think of anything. After all, I pointed out, Chinese Magwitch was only trying to help. He had a very pregnant wife – a father-to-be no less! – and he ran a successful business. It wasn't beyond the realms of possibility to imagine that we could also, once successful, help someone in the way he had helped us. It wasn't a bad system in its own way. It wasn't as if banks were ever bending over backwards to lend money to the penniless.

'It's karma,' Jessica said. 'They help us, and when we're on our feet we help someone else. Communism at its very best.'

Jessica had flirted with communism during our Liberal Studies classes in the Upper Sixth, all for effect of course. It was a sure way to impress the boys who came over from the grammar school: little green-blazered beetles in pungent aftershave edging up besides the girls in their black blazers, skirts and ties. Jessica was always one to declare an allegiance: I'm an Existentialist, a Buddhist, a Communist! The truth was, when you scratched the surface, she was Tory blue through and through. Despite her upbringing, Jessica believed in helping herself, not others. It wasn't a given that the Chinese would get their money's worth with her.

'So,' I said, 'we agree on the following: 1. Our restaurant owner is an honest family man, with a pregnant wife, and an established business – who we feel we can trust; 2. We intend to pay our rent, thus not offending said benefactor; 3. We are going to find successful high-powered jobs – we are young, English-speaking and keen, on the threshold of bilingualism; and 4. We can leave the house of Axel Blanchard and begin a life worthy of our academic studies.'

Jessica agreed and we chinked empty coffee cups. My stomach churned. It was one thing pledging such things here in the 19th *arrondissement*, far from the leafy western suburbs, but quite another thing having the balls to walk out on the family who had grown to depend on me.

'I guess I'd better tell Florence as soon as we get home,' I said.

Jessica spluttered on the last of her coffee froth.

'*Tell* her?' she cried. 'What do you mean *tell* her! Imagine the stress we'll have to endure in the next few days. We need to source furniture, beds, jobs. We can't be working out our notice with Florence in the loop. Imagine the black looks and moods *that* would entail. We don't have contracts; we're slave labour when you think about it. Well, this is payback time. It's what you get when you take on casual labour: casual labour does a bunk when it gets a better offer.'

'But aren't they *fond* of us?'

'*Fond* of us! Are you kidding? We're a pound of flesh, paid for under market value. That's all. Two skivvies.'

She sounded like a trade unionist now. Jessica was good at rousing a crowd.

'So, what do we do?'

'We leave in our own time,' Jessica said. 'In the dead of

night. We'll do a midnight flit if we need to. There's no time for sentiment here, not when our lives are at stake. We've given our word, we've taken that flat and now the clock is ticking for rent.'

To remind me of the gravity of our situation she raised her hand to her mouth and carefully folded in her middle finger.

On our return to the metro we found a cheap shop which sold an array of household goods at cost: plastic tablecloths, buckets, brooms and mop heads. Outside, propped up against a row of clothes dryers there were two camp beds. The Arab man who ran the shop showed us how easily the legs folded in and how the beds could be carried like oversized deckchairs. He seemed to think we were going camping and tried to sell us a gas stove and a groundsheet for good measure. Jessica, proving my point about never opening her purse unless she needed to, opened it now to pull out yet another crisp note, telling me I could pay her back when I started work ... with interest. We bought two beds and a quilt cover each. It was decided we'd invest in the actual quilts themselves in winter. The quilt covers were amazingly cheap: only ten francs, like most of the other articles in the shop. I chose a peach and turquoise pattern, almost paisley, and Jessica a plain white cover.

We carried the beds and our quilt covers back up to the apartment, stopping at the corner shop to buy a bottle of red screw-top wine, a packet of plastic knives and forks, a crusty baguette which felt at least a day old, a packet of Babybel cheese and a squishy garlic-flavoured Boursin. It was our first meal in our new home. We sat on the floor with the windows open and feasted on the baguette and cheese, snapping frail plastic knives as we buttered hunks of hard bread, the wine staining our tongues bilberry blue as we got drunker and sillier by the minute. I'd grown careless of the time, aware that I should already be back home in The Submarine ironing. Instead, I lay prostrate on my new bed, which I'd prised open (nearly amputating three fingers) and placed in my designated corner of the flat, bathing in the warm sunshine that flooded through the windows. I felt (almost) free.

As we examined the apartment and its kitchen we realised how much we required to get started. The kitchen was devoid of a table, or an oven. The built-in cupboards were empty of glasses or crockery. We'd need to buy everything from scratch, 'or eat out' as Jessica said. Peeling the red plastic from a portion of Babybel cheese I stretched out in contentment. There was a real sense of achievement in being here at number 27, rue Eugène Jumin. It was the start of our Parisian adventure. I didn't need David: he was welcome to his grass-skirted lover. I was here, under my own guise, in central Paris and within spitting distance of Montmartre and its cobbled streets.

There would be much Seizing of the Day, novel-writing, and late-night parties with candles flickering on the chimney breast. We would fill the tiny bathroom cabinet with our cosmetics and crowd in to get ready on a Friday night with a glass of wine. I'd finally be doing all the things I should have done at university when I'd been busy getting engaged and pretending to be grown-up before my time. This was to be a chapter in my life devoted to all the many things I'd missed out on as a teenager, when Dad had either been working nights and needing peace and quiet or re-enacting the usual long and heavy dramas played out with my mother. Back home I was the adult and my parents the children: smashed window panes, slashed wrists, shouts and screams; whispered phone calls in the dark. My brother Steven and I had tiptoed through the debris of our parents' marriage and escaped into our books.

University had never felt like home. Academically it had been a disappointment after sixth form and the wonderful teachers I had left behind. There had been few, if any, moments to inspire at Aberystwyth, unless you counted the sexy American Literature tutor who smoked joints while he read Walt Whitman and described the sensual baths he took with his wife after making love to her on the beach.

This would be the first home to call my own as an adult, albeit shared with Jessica, and in a foreign city, no less! A place of promise. We might have had a small brush with the Chinese underworld to get here – but they had our best interests at heart. Our fingers would be safe; our lives were just beginning.

I was in my room later that night, sorting through old letters and papers in preparation for our grand departure when Delphine knocked and let herself in. She should have been in bed hours ago, but I didn't have the

A French life: Book One

heart to tell her off. She sidled on to the bed beside me and started sorting through my make-up bag.

'Mummy knows about the postcard you sent to Marcel,' she said in English. 'He told her. You are in love?'

I reddened, cursing the day I'd sent that stupid missive.

'I'm happy for you,' she said after a moment. 'Mummy not so much, but I thought if you like Marcel that's a *good* thing. You won't leave us at the end of the year.'

'I thought you didn't want any more au pairs – eggs in the shoes and all that. What difference does it make if I leave?'

Delphine smiled.

'I like you and Jessica,' she said. 'You are the only *jeune fille au pair* crazy enough to send love letters to mummy's boyfriends.'

'Friend, you mean,' I said, 'In English we only say boyfriend when you are in love. Or dating.'

The girl shrugged. 'This lipstick's nice. Can I try it on?'

I couldn't face saying goodbye in person and I realised it was because of the children. Who would have thought it? Maybe, despite the convictions I had held close at heart since that first viewing of 'Gorillas in the Mist', I wasn't only cut out to look after primates after all. I wondered who would next move into my room to care for Florence's children. It was a strange thing to be such an intimate, underwear-ironing part of the family for so many months and yet not truly belong in any way; to feel both at home and not at home; part of the family and yet a stranger. In some ways, I'd been more present in this house over the past few months than Florence herself. I'd learnt how to iron shirts and how to smother a chicken in olive oil and stuff an onion up its bum. I knew the smell of the house, from the shoes I polished each night, to the scent of the fabric conditioner I poured into the machine. While Florence had been at her atelier, pretending that she was not the bourgeois wife of an upper-class businessman, I'd been here, playing *her* role. I knew now what it would be like to have children, or almost. I had a much clearer idea of what it was like to run a house and home, and a fair notion of what it meant to be a wealthy French woman in the western suburbs of Paris. I didn't think I'd ever employ a *jeune fille au pair*.

Jessica and I waited for Florence to return from her drumming-class and grew tipsy on a bottle of wine filched from the cellar. We both needed a bit of Dutch courage. It was just as well we were leaving, stocks were running low, and we'd resorted to drinking dusty old bottles from the sixties, made by someone called Petrus Pomerol, pushed to the back of the cellar and surely past their sell-by date.

Earlier that evening, I had crept across the garden lawns to observe the now empty cottage. Jessica's case was by the door ready to be brought up to the main house and hidden in the garden. The rubbish she had accumulated during her stay had been bagged and binned round the back. She'd left a postcard saying '*Merci*' on the fireplace. I intended to leave my own note on the kitchen table in case Florence thought I'd been kidnapped.

Florence returned from drumming around ten. She looked exhausted, holding both rails with her long, delicate arms as she hoisted herself up the stairs. She barely acknowledged us, her eyes fluttering beneath their pale butterfly-thin lids. I knew she would switch on the shower and freshen up before Axel returned home. He was late tonight.

Most likely, it would be Monsieur Blanchard who would find my note first. I imagined him pounding up the stairs and crashing into the eastern wing with the bad news, wondering how his wife would cope now that their domestic life had been thrown into disarray. I wondered why I was still worrying about the children's routine, still unable to switch off from my duties. Earlier, when I had tucked the children up in bed, I gave Clémence a special hug. She didn't want to take out her sparkly butterfly clips and for once I said nothing. Baptiste jumped into his bed with a copy of *Tintin*, oblivious as always to what was going on around him. I wished he'd look up, so I could remember him, but he didn't. Only Delphine seemed to sense that something was wrong, coming down twice to see if we were still in the kitchen, wanting to sit at the table and hang on to our every word. At last, Jessica dispatched her to bed with false promises of a girlie chat another night. This felt wrong. It all felt wrong, but we were in too deep to change our minds.

I had accumulated a lot of bags and needed help. We

listened for the sound of the shower running in Florence's quarters and once we were sure the coast was clear raced up the stairs to fetch my stuff. We began our descent down three flights of stairs laden like Spanish donkeys. As we reached the bottom flight, in direct line with the front door, we saw a familiar shadow and heard a key turn in the lock. Axel.

I froze as he came in through the door. Caught in midaction, I was horrified and ready to confess. Sensing this, Jessica kicked me from behind in warning. He saw us both and smiled in an unusually warm manner, displaying a full set of teeth and his 'cheeky boy' smile. It must have been a good day.

'Having a sort out?' he asked in perfect English. 'That's right,' says Jessica. 'Out with the old!"

But Axel had already lost interest and didn't answer. He bounded up the stairs two at a time, to see his wife. I knew he would take off his tie, loosen his top button, hang his jacket on the clothes rack and reappear ten minutes later to pour himself an evening drink. Florence would come down to join him, freshly showered, wearing an innocent white cotton dress, her African drumming trousers thrown in the wicker basket for me to wash.

Jessica bundled me out of the garden gate like a bag lady, retrieving her own case from beneath the laurel bush where she'd hidden it. It was only once we were halfway to the train station that I realised the note I'd written for Florence was still in the pocket of my dress. I told Jessica.

'Too late now,' she panted. 'The bird has flown.'

The train journey to our new apartment involved a

change of metro line at the Gare du Nord, a sprawling international station attracting hordes of passengers both day and night. The trains to and from La Gare du Nord were packed. Frequently I was thrown up against an unwashed body, or groped by a wandering hand.

Porte de la Villette, our new home area, wasn't the safest part of town in the late eighties, although the apartment was beautiful and even this area beyond our means. Twenty-five years on the area has been spruced up. At the time when we moved in, it was still in that part of town where girls tried to avoid travelling home alone. Stories about aggression towards women were rife amongst au pair girls in the city. The streets were full of *sans-abri*; those literally *without shelter*, lost souls who slept on the ventilation grids of the metro for warmth, blasted by gusts of warm air from the bowels of the underground, frozen topside during the long, cold Parisian winters. A network of arteries ran beneath the city, and sometimes as my train halted between stations, I glimpsed a community of *sans-abri* bedded down in the offshoots to the main tunnel where the trains no longer travelled: groups of men clustered together, drinking methylated spirits, kipping on old sacking, a stone's throw away from the rats who foraged by the side of the tracks. It was a world away from the western suburbs, the Blanchard's house, the unaffordable boutiques above our heads in the 16th arrondissement or on the Champs Elysées.

The northern line of Paris was a particularly intrepid line, but Jessica and I reminded ourselves that it was only a short flight, as the Paris pigeon flew, to the soft, bosom-like domes of the Sacre Coeur, visible from almost anywhere in the city, and to our favourite restaurant and a bowl of warm and comforting French onion soup. To my romantic mind, nothing could spoil the beauty or the magic of Montmartre and I comforted myself with the knowledge that our new home lay in its shadow just a heartbeat away. We were not far from the tourist attractions such as the Moulin Rouge and the Place du Tertre. But in Paris, no-one was ever far away either from the sex shops and the rows of seedy boutiques where leather curtains flapped like ravens' wings as we passed, and squat men huddled at trestle tables, fingering tickets that promised peep shows with three or more girls for the price of one. Paris had many faces and I was beginning to know them all.

CHAPTER 16

Our first few nights at 27 rue Eugène Jumin were idyllic. The weather was still warm for September and with both windows flung wide open, we could hear the music floating in from the jazz festival at the Porte de Pantin. Apart from our camp beds and new quilt covers there wasn't a stick of furniture in the flat. We sat cross-legged on the floor, careful not to get crumbs on the sheets, uncharacteristically house-proud now that we had a home of our own. We bought most of our food from a small corner shop run by a Moroccan man called Mahdi (which was pronounced the same as Tuesday in French), who treated us like locals.

We were careful with our money. Our only financial resources were those left in Jessica's purse. Because of our prudence, we washed our plastic knives and forks and lined them up on the draining board as if they were silver. Our menus followed much the same pattern. We couldn't make anything hot without an oven and discovered the difficulties of chopping ingredients for a salad without a proper knife. The plastic knives bent and snapped under the slightest pressure. It was a curious experience biting into an onion as if it were an apple. We resorted to eating finger foods: crusty bread which could be broken off by hand; Babybel cheese, which was a favourite as it could be peeled like a banana; packets of squishy Boursin that could be spread with knife, fork, or finger; and screw-top wine. I'm not entirely convinced that the cheap, plastic-bottled wine Jessica swore by wasn't designed to unblock drains. It left our breath reeking like the old man who slept on the bench in the metro with his dog. I could see that Jessica's teeth had begun to absorb the colour and had the same permanently plum veneer as her lips and tongue.

But our money was running out. Not only this, but our clothes needed washing. Jessica had worn the same floral dress for the past few days and I'd got through most of my clean clothes. There was a distinct difference between the fresh smelling laundry which I ironed back in The Submarine and the clothes which now lay in a plastic bag by the side of my bed. There was a launderette at the end of the street, but I'd have to borrow money from Jessica, and she didn't seem as concerned about clean clothes as I was, saying I shouldn't fuss.

In desperation, I pleaded for some coins from Jessica to phone my dad from a telephone kiosk at the station. I knew his work number and I wanted to ask him if he could send some emergency funds. I had to make this sound like a temporary blip. He promised to send me the equivalent of £50 in francs. He was pleased we'd got a flat, though I didn't mention the Chinese connection. 'Get yourself a job,' he said. I didn't mention returning to England as a possibility as both of us knew this wasn't an option. I knew my dad was waiting for my brother Steven to start university in a year's time before leaving home himself. He had been unhappily married for twenty-seven years and I'd been party to his secret for years: *When you and your brother are both at Uni and gone, I'm off. I've done my bit.* I couldn't blame him. My mother's drinking, her obsessions, her violent outbursts and her fear of 'germs' had grown worse over the years. She wouldn't admit there was a problem to treat. My father was too afraid to talk to the doctor; afraid not only of his wife but also that she could appear so normal 'on tap', that he might not be believed. *Most blokes wouldn't have lasted a year.* That's what her brother had said. My uncle, like most other members of our family, had learned to keep his distance.

I'd never had a relationship with my mother. We had never touched or kissed or hugged. She clung to my brother; her self-proclaimed favourite child. It wasn't a position I envied and I wondered how my brother would ever escape. From the safety of Paris, I felt sick at the thought of who would care for my mother if Dad carried out his plans. I couldn't blame him. No-one could, not if they'd experienced the home life we'd lived. I needed to find a job. The only person who could look after me, was me.

We didn't have a landline and had no way of contacting

friends before the invention of mobile phones. Evenings were spent at the flat, without a TV or radio for company, cut off from the outside world, apart from the non-stop jazz music which played in the park opposite. We hadn't met any other neighbours in the block of flats. There was one door at the end of our corridor next to our own and this was permanently shut. There was a man's name by the bell, Henri Martin, underneath which he had scrawled the word *journaliste* on a small white card.

For entertainment, we relied on conversation and books. Jessica was reading *The Unbearable Lightness of Being*, as well as her sacred anthology of Beckett. I was finishing *The Woman in White*, which had me gripped. As always, books were a blessing and an escape.

I was hungry. All day I'd been haunted by visions of the roast chicken I made for the children at the Blanchard house. Jessica seemed to fare on a diet of black coffee and pure alcohol. I'd grown used to four meals a day over the past few months, including the array of pastries and cheeses for afternoon *goûter*. My stomach had expanded along with Clémence's pot belly and was struggling to shrink back down to the size required by our current state of penury.

I was on the final chapter of my book, when a strange tap-tapping noise sounded on the stairs. Jessica jumped from her bed and switched out the light. The siren of a passing ambulance drowned out the noise for a moment, but then there was a loud rap at the door. She shot to my side of the room.

'It's *him,*' her stained red lips mouthed.

'Who?' I asked, but she clamped her hand over my mouth and hissed into my ear: 'Shut the fuck up, will you!'

Our visitor banged more loudly on the door this time, and tried the handle for good measure.

'It's Chinese Magwitch with the high-heeled boots,' she hissed again.

This explained the tapping on the stairs.

'Our benefactor? How can you be sure? Lots of men wear boots.'

'He's been here once today already, when you were out phoning your dad.'

'What? Shouldn't we let him in? He must know we're here!'

'NO!' She looked frightened.

'Why not? And why the hell didn't you tell me he'd been here?'

'He said not to, and I wondered if the flat might be bugged.' She did that annoying thing with the folded-in finger again.

'Stop being stupid for a minute. What did he want?' There was a silence.

'*Me.*'

'You?'

'Yes, you know. *Me.* Sex of course!'

'But his wife's pregnant! Surely not?' I paused in fear. 'What about me?'

'No, he doesn't want you.' 'Thank fuck for that!'

'He doesn't like blondes.' 'Small mercies!'

She looked scared now. 'It's all very well, blondie, but

I'm the only brunette in here.'

We jumped as the sound of a key was inserted in the lock. Luckily our own key was on our side of the door firmly blocking the hole. The good thing was that Magwitch couldn't get in. The bad thing was he knew we were on the other side. We heard a voice calling out in French. Jessica pulled the quilt cover over us and we sat for a time. Just when I thought the siege would never end, the footsteps tip-tapped down the stairs, gradually disappearing all together. We crawled out from beneath our makeshift tent and Jessica went to the door to open it. She said she wouldn't be able to sleep unless she was sure Magwitch had gone for good.

I heard a small cry and realised she was pulling something in from the landing. It was a rectangular box all wrapped up and taped in plastic. A box of drugs perhaps? Maybe they wanted us to trade cocaine? Or guns? The door was wide open and strung from the handle I saw a smaller white plastic bag, knotted at the top. It felt warm. Jessica ripped and tugged at the wrapping and the strong white tape. My mind flashed back to memories of Christmas with my brother when we would pull gifts excitedly from our pillow cases on Christmas morning. Inside the box there was an electric hot plate with two rings and a plug. Jessica carried it over to the kitchen and plugged it in, turning both knobs. Within seconds the two hot plates had lit up crimson red. We had heat.

'We should leave it outside; refuse it!' I said.

But Jessica was busy opening the plastic bag now. Inside

there were two small white cartons of hot Chinese soup, a bag of six spring rolls, a sprig of fresh mint, and a wicker basket of small white dumplings filled with prawns. Rolled up in a serviette at the bottom were six hard sesame-seed biscuits. Her eyes caught mine with that same gleam I remembered from school, when the monotony of a history lesson was interrupted by the sound of the metal shutters to the school canteen squeaking open at noon.

'Get the cutlery, Marilyn.' she said.

Over the following week, a series of food parcels were left knotted to our door handle: sweet and sour pork; curried frogs' legs; and spicy prawn curry. Each time these parcels were accompanied by a bundle of sesame-seed biscuits, which we nibbled when stocks were low. Jessica had invested in a pan and we heated water on the stove. Instant coffee and sesame biscuits in the morning; tea and sesame biscuits at four; hot chocolate and sesame biscuits before bed. Whatever else we found on the door handle formed the bulk of our weekly diet.

The food parcels never arrived at the same time, which kept us on our toes. One of the deliveries occurred when we were out in the city and we realised that Chinese Magwitch had been into the flat. A can of tinned lychees sat ominously on the counter.

'Are you sure he wants to use you as a sex slave?' I asked Jessica. 'So far he's doing a pretty good impression of the Red Cross.'

But my friend was adamant. 'You weren't here that day,'

she snarled. 'He made it very clear what he wants. And he'll be back to try his luck again – you mark my words. Not to mention the rent which we still don't have.'

Neither of us had made any headway finding jobs. Our first foiled attempt at finding employment had ground our egos into the splattered, dog-turd pavements of Paris. For the first time since sixth form I worried that we were not that special at all. There was no guarantee of anything in life, despite what we thought, especially not because we happened to be the first children in our families to make it to university. On first leaving the Blanchard household we'd clung onto our academic egos (despite my miserable 2:2). This over-inflated sense of our worth was a throwback from school. Jessica and I decided that our initial job only needed to be a means to an end. If we could pay our first month's rent and keep our fingers intact we'd have time to perfect our CVs and find proper employment soon enough.

Chanting our *carpe diem* mantra, Jessica marched into the local supermarket, me in tow, reassuring me that wearing a red uniform and cap that said 'CASINO' wasn't *so* bad. Anyway, it wouldn't be for ever.

'What are we going to do?'

'I don't know,' she said. 'Sit at the till, stack shelves? Who cares, if it gets us out of that flat.' She'd been jittery of late, freezing every time the door banged closed in the foyer downstairs. Chinese Magwitch had rattled her more than I thought. She looked frayed and unkempt.

The supermarket was packed. There was a row of girls at the checkout counters, hair tied back beneath red

Casino caps, beeping away at articles while rows of frazzled shoppers packed their goods. Small French supermarkets like this one were traditionally scruffy around the edges. Stray lettuce leaves lay on the black-and-white floor tiles, there were puddles of water round the fish section and kids skidding up and down the aisles with miniature trolleys decked with poles and red warning flags. Jessica walked up to the *Accueil* and asked to speak to the manager. Five minutes later a man with a badge saying *Xavier* emerged from the back. His sleeves were rolled up as if he'd been stock-taking.

'*Oui, qu'est-ce qu'il y a?*'

We've come about jobs, Jessica said in her best French. The man looked us up and down and asked if we had worked in a supermarket before. Jessica raised her shoulders and tossed him her Maggie Thatcher look.

'It can't be *that* hard,' she said. '*Ce ne peut pas être si compliqué que ça?*'

This wasn't perhaps the best tactic. Xavier was immediately offended. It might have been better to have looked interested in his shop, instead of telling him any old chimpanzee could work there. He smiled, and for a second I was relieved, but then I realised it's what the French called *un rire jaune* – a 'yellow smile': sarcastic and insincere.

'You know how to work a till?'

'*Non, pas encore.*'

'You have experience unpacking the trucks and loading the shelves?'

'*Non.*'

'You are familiar with the home-brands of supermarket chains like this one?'

'*Pas du tout*'

'But you want to work here?' '*Oui.*'

'And what makes you think you would be any good?'

Jessica's mouth froze open like the beached tuna fish on ice we'd just seen. I stepped in.

'We need to pay our rent. We're desperate. We'll do anything. Even mop the floor.' I pointed at the soggy piece of lettuce beneath the man's shoes.

'*Je suis désolé,*' he said, 'some of the women here have fifteen years' experience. *Nous n'avons rien pour des filles comme vous.*'

'What does he mean he's got nothing for *girls like us*?' I asked outside the shop.

'Oh, he thinks we're dykes,' Jessica said breezily.

This was not the first time that Jessica and I had been mistaken for a lesbian couple, which I could only presume was because of our clothing. One night we had tried to gain free access to a nightclub in the city, near the rue de Rivoli, only to be told by the bouncer on the door that: '*Ce n'est pas un club pour des gouines.*' This is not a club for 'dykes'. We'd spent all that previous day out at the park in Versailles, and I'd been bullied by Jessica into wearing a long, floral print dress like hers. When we got to the park we'd re-enacted scenes of Marie-Antoinette skipping in her gardens at the Hameau de la Reine, taking photographs of ourselves tripping over the bridge at the lake, or posing wistfully in the orchards. Jessica insisted on asking a tourist to take a photograph of her with her head on a tree stump while I mimed her decapitation. The German who took our picture found it funny, but others tut-tutted in disapproval. We'd gone straight into town from Versailles still wearing our long flowing dresses and straight to the nightclub door. The bouncer looked us up and down in disapproval. Most of the other girls were wearing tight, sexy little numbers. We clearly weren't worthy of free entrance. Clothes counted for a lot in Paris, and in his eyes we looked like hippie, vegetarian lesbians. There were clubs for girls who dressed like we did, the man on the door told us, but his place wasn't one of them.

We walked home from the Casino supermarket defeated. Jessica bought a plastic bottle of wine from Mahdi for consolation. The cheapest in the shop. Back at school my French teacher, renowned for his side burns and adenoids, had snottily menaced a life spent on a supermarket checkout, unless I got myself an education. But the sad fact was, that even *with* an education, we weren't good enough for the job. For *any* job. Okay, phoning the Opéra Garnier had been a little optimistic, but surely the supermarket guy could have given us a chance?

We were almost home when Jessica grabbed my arm. There was a black, four-wheel drive outside number 27 and a dapper man in black boots was getting out. It was Chinese Magwitch clutching a white plastic bag. We ran back towards the metro without a word, escaping into the safety of its gaping mouth, collapsing breathlessly by the

ticket office and dragging the stale underground air into
our lungs with relief.

CHAPTER 17

A week later I was sitting in a temping office in Gare Saint Lazare looking at a heavily made-up French woman with dyed blonde hair and black roots. It had been a week which had seen the delivery of food parcels galore: bags of soggy white dumplings, chicken Chow Mein, prawn crackers, plastic containers of beef noodle soup and enough sesame-seed biscuits to cause a peak on the nut commodities market. My breath smelt of curried prawn. And it was only nine o'clock.

The women at the agency looked me up and down in the same way as she might examine an object retrieved from a blocked kitchen sink.

'You don't have a CV?' she asked. '*Non.*'

'You can type?'

'*Oui.* I learnt on a machine when I was seven. I can touch-type.'

She looked pleased and leant forwards on both elbows. Her lipstick had run into the crack around her mouth.

The butt-end of a cigarette smouldered in the green Cinzano ashtray on her desk.

'So, you are familiar with WordPerfect and Lotus 1-2-3, I presume?'

'No, I've never used a computer. I didn't do Computer Science at school. I did Drama and English.'

She waved a hand impatiently. 'But you said you could type?'

'Yes, on a machine. A real machine. You know, a Remington.'

She sighed. Impatient now.

'And are you, or are you not, *bilingual*?' 'Not.'

The conversation had been held in English to prove this very point.

'But you tell me you have been working for a French family in the suburbs, so you must have spoken some French?'

'Oh yes, to the younger children mainly. The eldest daughter could speak English.'

She smiled to show the gaps in her teeth which were filled with black plaque.

'So, you *can* speak in French.'

'Well, I can tell you it's time for your bath and not to forget to wash your hair; I can ask you if you want an Alice-band or plaits, or what you want for dinner. Oh, and I also know the name of lots of Chinese food in French.' The plastic bags on our door handle were conveniently labelled in French with a black marker pen.

The woman shook her head, earrings jangling, and picked up her cigarette for a last drag before stumping it out hard on a cushion of earlier corpses, the tip of each Marlboro scored with red lipstick around the filter.

'But could you manage the diary of a top French professional and type his letters and manage his accounts?'

'His name's not Axel, is it?' 'No, it is not.'

'Oh, good. Well, to be honest, probably not.'

She was losing patience now. It was time for her own *carpe diem* speech.

'Listen, you are clearly not stupid. You have been to University you tell me, n'est-ce pas? You have learnt a considerable amount of French in a very short period, now you must pull yourself together, as I did when I was your age. If you do not know how to do something, you keep quiet, you look around you and you observe how others are managing. Soon you will learn. This is what you must do in life to survive. This is what I myself was obliged to do on my first day in an office. Had I run away crying like a baby, I would not be here now. *Vous comprenez, mademoiselle?*

My main understanding was that the woman was anxious for her commission with the company for whom she was recruiting and that she was prepared at this point to throw me into the lion's den, whatever my qualifications. As if reading my thoughts, she added somewhat slyly, 'You will be paid for however many days you are retained, so even if it doesn't quite work out, there will be some money.'

The woman in the Saint Lazare temping agency pointed to a map of Paris on her wall and to the westerly tip and the white Arche of La Défense. I felt like Edmund as he stood with the White Witch in *The Lion, the Witch and the*

Wardrobe. What choice did I have? And even if they paid me for a day's work before booting me out it was better than nothing.

'You will go then?'

'Alright. Do I need to sign something?'

The next morning, I caught the RER A line to La Défense, dressed smartly in a white shirt with a black pencil skirt and Jessica's black high-heeled shoes. Her suitcase was stuffed with an array of garments purchased from Oxfam and more suitable to a theatrical department: a fox stole, a mangy fur coat, sixties' shoes and gloves. Not so long ago I'd cringed at the thought of wearing someone else's castoffs. It was bad enough knowing that Jessica had yellowed the armpits of the shirt without wondering who else's sweat lay engrained in the cotton; possibly someone now dead who had leaked body fluids between the stitches. I had a strict rule about wearing an article of clothing only once, but our current living conditions had meant that I'd had to reign in my latent hygiene phobias.

The metro was unbearably hot and the skirt, which was part wool, was itchy. I was a commuter now, one of thousands, travelling to my office in Paris. In my bag, there was a purse, currently empty, my *carte orange* train pass, and my passport. I didn't know what else I should bring. A notepad and pen perhaps?

I came up the escalator to the Parvis de la Défense. A huge esplanade stretched before me. Dotted all around were the sky scrapers of Paris. La Tour Elf, La Tour Atlanta, the CNIT, as well as Les Quatre Temps: a sprawling shopping centre. I was busy looking at my map, trying to work out where the Washington Tower was situated, when I heard someone call my name.

'Karen, Karen! *Ici!*'

My first instinct was to keep on walking. I'd been hiding from Magwitch for so long that although it was a female voice, I couldn't imagine that being recognised in the city could augur anything good.

'Karen, *arrête! C'est moi!*'

It was a voice I was used to obeying, and eventually I stopped and turned. Leaning on her crutches at the top of the steps to the underground, in her baggy African trousers (un-ironed), with an army jacket slung around her shoulders over a flimsy T-shirt, was Florence! She looked like a busker, or any one of the itinerants in the metro liable to shove an empty cap into your face for loose change. My face flushed with shame. Running away was all very well when you thought you wouldn't have to see the person you'd run away from ever again, but here I was on my way to meet my new employer, face to face with the old one I'd just abandoned. I wondered wildly if Florence had been to see my new employer. If she'd handed in a stinking reference, saying how unreliable I was, and how I didn't work out my notice. Or if Axel had hung a pile of un-ironed shirts onto the office door handle.

'*Bonjour*, Florence,' I said.

Florence flung her arms around me. When I pulled

away I saw that her eyes were filled with tears. She was clutching a bunch of small printed leaflets. She pushed one into my hand. On it there was a picture of me in my baggy blue and white Mary Poppins dress. Underneath there was a typed description in English and French: 'Slim, blonde girl in her early 20s. Terrible French. MISSING. *PERDUE.*' Like someone's pet poodle. My cheeks started to burn. I hadn't been kidnapped, I'd gone voluntarily to live with the Chinese Mafia and was in their debt cooped up in a posh flat in the 19th *arrondissement* and made fat on spring rolls and dried sesame-seed biscuits. Not only that, I was running late. I was expected on the 31st floor of the Tour Washington to meet the Head of Human Resources of an American software company.

Florence grabbed my arm and launched into a tirade as to how the children were pining for me; how they refused to have another *jeune fille au pair* in the house; how Delphine missed our late-night chats with Jessica. Where had I been living? Had I been sleeping rough? (*Did I look that bad?*) Why did I leave? Was it something she'd or said done to offend me? And then there was the matter of my last wages which I'd left without collecting. Florence told me that she had been coming here to La Défense, and to many of the other main train station exits of Paris, to look for me. I said that I was fine. *Merci beaucoup.* And that I'd been sharing a flat with Jessica, although I didn't tell her my address. I'd got a job, I said, and I was going to be late if I didn't get a move on. Florence trailed beside me, clutching my arm like a street urchin. I was so smartly dressed in comparison that a passer-by turned and raised his eyebrows to see if I needed help. Finally, having reassured her that I was not dead, and having categorically refused all offers to return to the house, I agreed to keep in touch, promising that one day, when I was settled in my new job, I would go back to the house to sleep in my old bed and to see the children.

I would see Florence and the children again over the years, returning to the house to sleep in the comfort of The Hessian Sack on several occasions. The last time I saw her, I was a mother myself with a young baby in my arms. After my last visit, the family moved away, and we lost touch. I searched for Florence years later but found no trace of her. Perhaps she had finally bolted herself, changed her name, or gone away for good. That day outside the RER station, I pulled away with more confidence than I felt, not entirely convinced that I shouldn't slip my hand into Florence's and go back home with her like a naughty schoolgirl. I strode ahead, trying to look as if I knew where I was going, though we both knew I hadn't a clue.

Fortunately, I glanced up and saw a signpost for La Tour Washington. The road was a labyrinth of passageways which I followed to the foot of the tower and to a glamorous entrance hall with a security desk. I handed over my ID and was given a badge and told to go through one of the security turnstiles and to take the elevator on my right to the top floor.

My meeting was with a woman by the name of Blandine Calmelane. I waited in the foyer until she came to collect me and led me to her office. Madame Calmelane was a tall, elegantly dressed French woman in a vibrant blue skirt and jacket. Her stiletto shoes jabbed the carpet as we passed reception, where I noticed a brown-haired girl hastily remove a bottle of nail varnish from the counter and endeavour to look busy. Madame Calmelane's hair was set in a glamourous cut reminiscent of Crystal Carrington in *Dynasty*. It was clear she commanded the respect of her colleagues, as several business men jumped aside or rushed to open a series of double doors so that we could pass. She showed me into her office and we sat at a smooth mahogany desk. The window was a picture frame to the whole of La Défense. In the distance the Eiffel Tower scored the horizon.

'So, you are seeking employment as a secretary, *n'est-ce pas? Vous avez apporté votre CV?*'

Contrary to what she asked, I hadn't brought a CV, believing that the temping agency had already secured a position for me.

'*Non. Je n'ai pas ça.*'

My French was clumsy.

'Hmm.' Madame Calmelane pushed her chair back on its little black wheels.

'*Vous parlez bien le français, je suppose?*' 'I'm getting better.'

I don't know why, but I replied in English.

'This is an American company, so your language skills are an advantage,' she replied, in perfect English. But then with a little smile added, 'We will, however, require a minimum understanding of French if you are to transcribe letters from our sales team. This wouldn't be a problem for you I take it? And your computer skills are up to speed?'

I remembered the woman's orders at the temping office and smiled confidently.

'Very well. Come with me.'

Madame Calmelane rose and led me back outside to an empty desk in an open office space. On the gleaming table, there was a small squat computer, which I later learnt was one of the original Macintosh SE models, circa 1987.

Madame Calmelane reached into an in-tray and placed a page of scrawl beside me.

'Type this for me, please,' she said. 'I'll be back in fifteen minutes. If you hurry, our porter will take it down to the mail room, so that it leaves today.'

She marched off and I stared at the page in dismay. French handwriting was notoriously difficult to read. If you weren't French it might as well be hieroglyphics. Everyone in France learnt to write in the same way. The Rs looked like Vs and the letters were formed in what appeared to be old-fashioned script to anyone from the UK. It was the sort of handwriting you might see on an old seventeenth-century document in a museum requiring a magnifying glass. I had no idea what the letter said. I decided to buy myself some time and try to work out how to switch the computer on.

This was the first time I had ever used a computer. At home, I'd had a manual and then an electronic type-writer into which I fed paper. My mother was a trained Pitman's touch hand typist, working for three years in a brewery before I was born. At the age of seven, keen to start writing a children's story, I'd been given a typewriter and a book explaining how to type. I'd persisted and grown proficient. Confident now of my skills, and with a typing speed of approximately sixty words a minute, I knew I wasn't completely useless. However, there were a few hurdles I hadn't expected. Not only could I not switch the computer on, but someone had moved all the letters into different places.

A few golden strands of hair fell to the desk. As I ran my hands through my hair a second cluster fell out. A few weeks later a local GP would tell me that this was down to stress, and that with a bit of luck it wouldn't all fall out, if I would only *calm down*. As matters stood, I was one pay packet off learning this, and I surveyed the clumps of blonde hair which lay on the desk in horror. I wasn't yet covered by the French health-care system. To aggravate the hair situation my hands had been itching non-stop for the last few days. I'd scratched them in my sleep and where the skin was inflamed, a row of weeping yellow sores had risen to the surface – more stress-related symptoms. The eczema, which had spread up both arms, wept and bled, then dried and cracked anew. It had worsened in the past few weeks with anxiety about money and how we were to survive. Working in a chic office in Paris with minimal nursery school French was turning into a harrowing experience. But I needed the money. Dad's money was almost all spent and I'd no means of paying my half of the rent. I couldn't fail this simple test. How hard could it be?

I ran my finger up and down the sides of the Mac and

finally found the 'on' button at the back. The machine
stirred into life with a series of judders and groans, like a
waste-disposal unit grinding metal. A black-and-white
screen flickered before me indicating a series of small files.
Other than the icon resembling Oscar's bin on *Sesame
Street* in the bottom right corner, I was unable to guess
what anything meant. Several members of staff walked
past my desk and stared at me, clocking the value of
my clothing; the cut of my hair, the worn heels of my
borrowed shoes. An unpleasant looking woman did
a double-take by my desk muttering, '*Who's she?*' to the
empty space around me. It was difficult to keep busy at
an empty desk when you hadn't a clue what to do.

After ten minutes of hair loss and skin irritation, I
was about to cry when Madame Calmelane returned.

'*Alors, ça y est?* Bertrand has already take the letter
downstairs perhaps?'

'No,' I confessed, hiding my hands under the desk. 'I
haven't even started. I've never used a computer before.'

'*Je vois.*'

She stared at me a moment and then swept to the
door with an imperious. '*Venez.*'

I followed Madame Calmelane out of the open-
space area, down a long corridor, past open doors
where salesmen lolled back in their chairs, feet on desks
or arms behind heads; past a pool of secretaries and
back to the main desk. At best, I expected Madame
Calmelane to shake my hand and show me to the lift.
The girl with long dark hair who was chatting into a
handset at reception looked up curiously. Madame

Calmelane waited until she had connected her call.

'This is Lisbeth,' she said, 'our *standardiste.*'

'*Bonjour,*' she said.

'Lisbeth, do you think you could train this candidate for me? If you train her well, I will offer you the vacant secretarial position which this girl is unqualified to accept.'

Lisbeth beamed. She was an attractive girl with dark brown eyes that matched her hair. She glowed with pleasure as if her headmistress had just awarded her position of head girl. The Head of Human Resources turned to me. Her regard was serious now.

'You have six weeks to learn,' she said. 'This is an important position as you are the first port of call for our clients, and for the type of job it is, very well-paid indeed. You must learn to master the *le standard* perfectly. You must transcribe messages *precisely*, so that the sales team can call back their clients immediately. There must be no mistakes with either name, number, or message. We are dealing with contracts worth hundreds of thousands of francs.'

Madame Calmelane relaxed a little, then added, 'It is perhaps fortunate for you that you remind me a lot of my daughter, who has just gone to London. I hope that someone there will show her the same kindness in a foreign country. However, much as I wish to be charitable, this is a multi-million-dollar business. Six weeks with no complaints from any members of my staff, or I will have no choice but to dismiss you. I will contact the agency with regards to your contract.'

I smiled as she turned from reception and left me to fend for myself.

I'd forgotten to ask exactly what a *standardiste* was.

CHAPTER 18

I was entrusted to Lisbeth for the rest of the day. Madame Calmelane took me back to her office so that I could fill in the necessary forms. She asked Lisbeth if she would be so kind as to take me to the canteen at lunch time. Divining that overall finances were tight, Madame Calmelane gave me a canteen card charged up with enough francs to buy a week's food. My mouth watered. Anything but Chinese! French fries, cheese, butter and chips; cutlery that didn't bend; plates that didn't sag.

Lisbeth's English was better than my French, owing to several trips to the States working in various bars and restaurants, and from her time as a ski-monitor on the ski slopes near her home town of Chambéry, where she confessed she had slept with enough English-speaking tourists to perfect her language skills. She was in her mid-twenties, tall and slender with long chestnut brown hair (which, unlike my own, was firmly implanted at the roots), and a deep throaty laugh with the underlying rasp of a chain smoker. She was attractive in an overly madeup way, her naturally oily face plastered in a coat of thick foundation to reduce   the shine. Her jeans were tight and her silk top clingy, turning the heads of the openly hot-blooded men in the queue as she bobbed above the switchboard. Lisbeth started by helping me acquire some new vocabulary. *Le standard* was the switchboard and we were *standardistes* or receptionists. The main switchboard connected 111 offices spread over the 31st floor, plus the hotline on the 24th floor, where clients called with technical problems from all over the world. The company sold mainframe software packages to some of the largest clients in France: Auchan and Carrefour hypermarkets, La Poste, the EDF national electricity company, etc. As an American company, we were affluent compared to local French businesses. On average, company salaries were thirty per cent above the minimum working wage (*le SMIC*) and I was to receive a whopping 9,000 francs a month. My previous salary as an *au pair* was mere pin money at 1,800 per month. If I could keep this job, I'd be able to pay my rent and finally have some money with which to enjoy Paris.

Despite our high working wage, Lisbeth and I were at the bottom of the company food chain. Below us were only two other staff members: Yazid Seridi, a Pakistani man whose English was better than his French, and his sidekick Bertrand Gauthier who smelt like a skunk because of something which Lisbeth described as '*a chronic and incurable and most sad problem with his glands (however often he washes, he will never remove the odour)*'. Yazid and Bertrand worked in the mail room and dealt with the packaging of software systems sent out from the office. They lived below ground in the cavernous dungeons *au sous-sol*. This was the lowest part of the building, an underworld five floors beneath the ground floor, reserved for the cockroaches and the mail men. Everyone below ground was male. There were no women in packing. Occasionally Bertrand travelled up in the lift to the 31st floor filling our nostrils with his acrid odour. Lisbeth mimed with a pinched nose how it was every employee's worst nightmare to be caught in the lift with the unfortunate man, especially if he alighted on the 24th floor leaving his odour behind him so that anyone catching a ride up to the 25–30th floors might wrongly attribute the provenance of the smell to the remaining person in the lift. She kept a special can of air freshener behind reception to fumigate the area post-mail delivery. We chatted at reception in broken English and French during those blissful moments when the monstrous *standard* drew breath between its ugly screeching howls. Bertrand and Yazid struggled through reception carrying a large box. There were at least fifty paces between us, but Bertrand's bitter smell hit my nostrils.

'Poor Yazid,' I said to Lisbeth.

'Poor *wife*,' said Lisbeth, 'though they appear happy.'

At twelve o'clock on the dot, Lisbeth unplugged the switchboard and we headed down for lunch.

The Tour Washington had three canteens, each on a different level below the entrance hall and descending in order of importance. Minus one housed a grand-sounding restaurant called Le Musée. Lisbeth told me that she had never eaten there because there was a non-spoken agreement that it was reserved for *cadres*. I was not familiar with the term, but during my time at Brown & Mclane Software, it was one that would come to haunt me.

We were, it transpired, *non-cadres*. *Cadre* was a title given to management and determined by pay scale and position within the company. *Cadres* were relinquished from the rules and regulations which controlled our lives and were trusted to manage their own time. They had higher salaries, better pensions, longer lunch breaks, and massive egos, considering themselves to be superior to *any other living creature on earth*. *Cadres* had graduated from the top business schools or universities in Paris, whereas *non-cadres* usually left school with little more than a *Brevet* or *Baccalauréat* beneath their belts. If that. Whatever the reality of our qualifications, our positions within the company predetermined the level of respect accorded to us from other members of staff, and by society at large. A *cadre*, it transpired, was not reprimanded for shagging his colleague on the boot of his car in the underground carpark to the same extent a *non-cadre* might be, if caught on CCTV. An incident between a randy head of department and his assistant filmed on the bonnet of a Peugeot 605 demonstrated such differences with clarity during my second week.

At the office, *non-cadres* (secretaries, receptionists, packers, cleaners, brown-collar workers, etc.) were obliged to use the formal '*vous*' when addressing their superiors on the pay scale, whereas *cadres* could happily use the familiar '*tu*', both to each other and when addressing *noncadres*. I learnt later on, that the informal '*tu*' could show friendship and familiarity, but when used unilaterally by a *cadre* it could also underline both inferiority and lower social status. Time taught me that, even when authorised, it was not always a good idea to jump in too soon with the friendly '*tu*', as it was difficult to revert to '*vous*' afterwards. An unmistakable snootiness could be conveyed with a well-placed '*vous*' enabling a much-appreciated chasm to exist between two parties. In-laws for example.

Later, I would learn that the use of '*vous*' in situations of intimacy, when '*tu*' would be the norm, could also heighten the eroticism of a moment, if so desired.

In many ways '*vous*' was far more flexible.

At the office, mistakes in tense were punishable by decapitation, since the *tutoiement* of a *cadre* showed the utmost lack of respect. I was going to have to revise all my verb endings, as clients on the phone had to be addressed in formal French and I'd spent the last few months with the Blanchards using the familiar '*tu*' form.

Lisbeth, Bertrand, Yazid and most of the other staff members at the office who deigned to talk to me, were *non-cadres*. I was about to join their ranks, so I needed to know the rules.

I learnt that the office building segregated its diners at luncheon in accordance to their social standing. With Le Musée occupying a rather grand space on level Minus One, there was a second canteen which was used by *non-cadres* on Minus Two. This restaurant catered for white-collar non-management staff: secretaries, lower-level accountants and technicians. Further below, on level Minus Three, in the entrails of the tower, there was another canteen which served only sandwiches and coffee. This was reserved for the lowest paid of all *non-cadres*: the packers, cleaners and security services, or the brown-collar workers. There were no seats, the workers huddling round a bar area long enough for a quick snack.

This tiered level of society surprised me. I'd thought that the French Revolution had taken care of all that. I'd imagined that it would be an 'all for one and one for all' type of mentality in France, considering the number of heads that had rolled into baskets. Not so. I was realising, first through the likes of the Blanchards and their easy aristocracy, and now through a software company in the heart of the business centre, that class was clearly defined and adhered to. There was a palpable sense at the office (albeit it American owned) of needing to learn one's place in the organisational chart and sticking to it. Contrary to the mentality I'd grown up with in my comprehensive school, social mobility was not encouraged.

A *non-cadre* when lying in the gutter (or eating at the canteen three floors below ground) shouldn't aim for the stars. It would only lead to unhappiness. When I joked with Lisbeth that one day we too might eat at *Le Musée* on Minus One, she looked at me in horror. Her greatest ambition was to achieve secretarial status, but she had no ambitions to eat caviar on toast from fine china side plates, bemoaning the fact that some of the sales team would struggle to accept her as a personal assistant, having first known her as a receptionist, never mind dining in her presence.

I asked Lisbeth what would happen if we decided to pay more and eat at *Le Musée*.

'This would be very bad form,' Lisbeth said. 'We might see our boss and she wouldn't like it.'

'Is the food nicer?'

'They have starters, main course, and dessert: pretty cakes with berries on the top, fresh not frozen; *foie gras* at Christmas. And a Roman statue at the entrance.'

I determined I would eat there one day. Even if I had to take my book and read in a corner by myself.

The food on Minus Two was school canteen fare: chips and lasagne. Hot stodge without a trace of those fine slices of salmon carpaccio that Lisbeth had talked of at *Le Musée*. Not a place where we were likely to find lemon quarters or bowls of hand-whisked mayonnaise. At least we weren't huddled round a cheese toastie at Minus Three with Bertrand and Yazid. At least it wasn't Chinese food.

As I trailed behind Lisbeth, up and down La Tour Washington and around the office, I observed how the *cadres* held the swing doors open for other *cadres*. Yet whenever a *cadre* met us on his travels, he pushed rudely past, allowing the door to swing wildly in our faces. (The majority of *cadres*, with the exception of Madame Calmelane, were male).

'Bit rude,' I said, checking my front tooth.

'*C'est normal,*' said Lisbeth. 'We are nothing to them. Rien du tout.'

On our first lunch together, Lisbeth ate a hearty lunch, swallowing a couple of yellow pills with her coffee.

'To keep thin,' she said. 'I used to have a fat ass. I was *obèse*, but now I'm on medication. They are trying to stop these pills now. They say they are bad for the heart – but I'd rather be dead when I'm old than fat like before.'

I noticed that she had that same American twang as Bonne-Maman when she said 'ass'.

After lunch, Lisbeth said she was going to have a cigarette, or '*une clope*' in familiar French *argot* (slang). This also helped to keep her weight down, and was a trick adopted by many of the French women I met. We went back up to the office. There were no rules preventing smoking in the building either in designated zones, or at their desks in the case of higher level management; and this regardless of the pregnant *non-cadres* who breathed the air around them.

At two o'clock precisely, Lisbeth plugged the switchboard back in. It jumped into life like a rabid dog, bouncing on the desk with the vibration of a hundred calls. The ear-piercing beeps were as strident as a baby hyena left to starve and could not be ignored. There were ten lines down the left-hand side of the machine and all of these were busy. Lisbeth skilfully put each call on hold with a well-practised '*Bonjour monsieur/madame. Un instant je vous prie.*' I practised the words, wondering if I would ever be able to speak as confidently to the clients as she did. From Lisbeth's easy banter and the twinkle in her eye, it was easy to see that a lot of the callers were like old friends, although she told me she had not met most of them.

'Many of our clients are based in Provence,' she said. 'but they know me now and we have a little chat when there is time.'

Lisbeth was a confident telephonist, with her flirtatious banter, her deep smoker's voice and gruff laugh. It was a facade which hid her insecurity. She explained to me in hushed tones that she couldn't spell, *at all*, having left school before her *Baccalaureate*. She told me that no-one would give her a chance in life, until she joined this company.

When she wrote messages in a childish hand with unnecessary loops and curls, the nib of her pen pressing deep into the paper, even I could pick up on a few basic mistakes: the use of the ER infinitive where a past participle should have been used. How would she manage with the razor-sharp-tongued women in the secretarial pool? Was social mobility such a good thing after all if it crushed your soul? Lisbeth was happy on reception, her bubbling personality rubbing off on even the dourest of staff members.

She showed me how to answer the calls and to put them through, before deciding halfway through the afternoon that it was time to leave me for yet another '*pause cigarette.*'

'You see how it works?' she said. The storm had died down in the last half an hour, following a frenzy of calls from irate accountants up and down the country who realised soon after a lazy lunch that they couldn't fathom their software package in time to meet their tight deadlines that evening. Lisbeth grabbed her Marlboro Lights from her bag, calling *'Je reviens,'* as she disappeared through the swing doors. The first call that came through was from the English office in the UK. I spoke to a pleasant-sounding man by the name of Mark Oakes and connected him through to the translation department with ease. Madame Calmelane passed by as I finished the call and smiled, reassured to see the situation under control.

The reception desk was an elegant semicircle which filled half the entrance hall. There was a giant yucca plant in a pot and a small waiting area with black leather sofas and IT magazines on a glass coffee table. The view from the window was spectacular: nothing short of the New York skyline to a country girl like me. Lost in contemplation and praying for Lisbeth's return, I sensed a presence by my side. It was Yazid. He sidled up to the desk, flicking an anxious look at the double doors which housed Human Resources and Madame Calmelane's bureau. In his hand, there was a box of yellow Post-its and a box of biros.

'Je t'ai apporté des fournitures,' he said, using the informal form of address straight off, which I knew was impertinent. Then, seeing that I didn't understand the word *fournitures*, said in English, 'Supplies, you know, for the office. I brought some. I manage mail and supplies.'

'Merci,' I said, and took them from him.

He didn't leave, but leant on the counter, with a contrived air of ease. It was clear to see that he wasn't comfortable on management level. Lisbeth had explained that all the offices around us were filled with the heads of sales, and other than the delivery of his supplies, there was no other reason for him to loiter. He should be back in the entrails of La Tour Washington. Yazid gave a nervous twitch as the door opened. A tall blonde salesman in a blue suit passed by with tanned features fresh from the côte d'Azur. We were invisible to him.

'Do you want to see Lisbeth?' I asked in French.

'No, no,' he said, slipping into English. 'It is you I want to see. I want to make you an offer.'

I hoped he wasn't going to ask me out. He must have been fifty. He took some time to *spit out his load*, as the French say, but finally reached the point:

'You have a British passport.' This was a statement not a question.

I was surprised. Yazid didn't oversee paperwork at the office. If I needed to renew my *carte de séjour* then surely Madame Calmelane would ask me. I didn't answer and seeing my confusion, he changed tack.

He smiled. 'You have just arrived in Paris, *n'est-ce pas?* Do you have a place to live yet?'

'Oh yes,' I said. 'That's all sorted.' If only he knew.

'Ah,' said Yazid, 'that's a pity. I could have helped. I know of a house, there are many rooms within.'

A bit like God's house then. 'No, I'm quite alright,' I said. 'This is your first job?'

'Yes.'

'Before that?'

'I took care of three children for a French family.'

Yazid jumped on this piece of information.

'Not much money. An *au pair* yes?'

'Yes, it was very badly paid,' I said, 'that's why I'm so grateful to Madame Calmelane for giving me a chance.'

At the sound of her name Yazid jumped into action, abandoning his stance as casual loiterer, spurred on like a Shakespearian messenger who was afraid that if he didn't get on with it, he might be felled at any moment.

'I cut to the point,' he snapped, 'but this is confidential. If you repeat this, I will be angry, *très faché*, and we don't want to get off on the wrong foot, right?'

More threats. I was terrified enough as to what our Chinese benefactor might do, without Yazid starting. I didn't say anything, wishing Lisbeth would hurry back. Even a client call would have been a relief.

'I can give you money,' Yazid said, 'money that you need to live here in Paris. But you would have to do something for me.'

'Really! Whatever do you think—!'

'It's not what you think,' he said quickly. 'You misunderstand, there is no sex involved. I am not this kind of man. In a way, you would be doing something good and kind. I don't know how many days you will be here, or if you stay for good. But I'm saying this now and the offer remains.'

'I don't understand what you want from me?'

'Your passport,' said Yazid bluntly. 'I know people, many people that need to get into the UK; good people, who want to work hard and make a living there. Not France. They want to go to England. Social Services are much kinder there.'

'What's that got to do with me?'

'You give me your passport,' he said, 'and you wait one month. This is very important. *Très, très important.* You wait one month before going to the Embassy and saying to the officials there that you have been very stupid. You had not realised your passport had gone from your purse. You must have dropped it. You make a declaration to the authorities, and all is well. Money will be given to you: £10,000. Not from me, but it will come. Pounds you understand. Not francs.'

I tried to speak but Yazid silenced me with a raised hand.

'Do not give me your answer now, there is no obligation. If you do not wish to, then we say no more about it. But it is a very generous offer. I ask only that you think seriously of your answer.'

I thought about Yazid's proposition for all of five seconds. It was not the first time in my life that an indecent proposal had been made; one which was morally questionable. Back when I was dating Steve I had been offered £5,000 to pose naked for a magazine with a graduation gown draped around my shoulders. Shocked to have been asked at the time, my inner devil whispered that it was just the amount I need to cover my Barclay's Bank overdraft. I knew it was something I would never do. Nevertheless, Steve's reaction had annoyed me: 'It'd be alright if I was the only one to see it,' he'd said. 'Bit of a laugh really, and we could do with the money. But what if my *father* were to see it?'

I'd asked Steve how likely it was that his father would purchase a copy of *Parade* magazine.

'Well, likely enough,' he'd replied. 'He's partial to the odd girlie magazine, you know.'

'Hypocrite!' I'd said, keen to provoke a dispute.

'No, I'm not,' he hissed, 'and you know it. You can't have your fiancée in that kind of a magazine.'

Faced with this deal from the Devil, I knew I'd no more sell my passport that I would pose naked in my graduation gown. I gave Yazid what I hoped was a cold stare. I was proud of my newly acquired passport with its deep blue cover and inner inscription where the Queen both *Requests and Requires* that I be allowed to pass freely *without let or hindrance, and afforded such assistance and protection as may be necessary*. I felt that Her Majesty was with me, caring for me on a daily basis, whatever French life might throw at me, and I wasn't about to betray that trust.

I wondered what Yazid was up to. The news was alive with the first Gulf War and there were talks of new terror attacks and of Scud missiles landing on French soil. There was increased security of late in Paris, and people in the metro wearing T-shirts which said, '*Non à la guerre.*' Madame Calmelane had told reception to be wary of all unmarked packages arriving at reception. As an American company, we were a target.

I thought about Yazid and the house in Paris with the many rooms which he had to offer, and the people who wished to gain access into the UK. Did they mean to be good citizens? Or did they want to infiltrate the country for sinister reasons? I wondered if there was something about me which attracted weird proposals: first our mysterious benefactor, and now this. As the French said, I must have '*pigeon*' written right across my forehead.

CHAPTER 19

My first few weeks on the switchboard were hell. I couldn't understand the names of the clients, the name of their companies or their telephone numbers. French numbers are a minefield. It was a given that Parisians were rude on the phone. Over the years, I have learnt that 99 per cent of all French people who answer the phone despise you before you've even begun. It's just the way it is. The customers were rude, but to be fair, so were the receptionists. It wasn't a winning combination. In my case, most of the callers were either irate, because the product they'd paid several million francs for wasn't working, or stressed because they were on the point of signing a million-dollar deal and afraid they might be making a mistake.

Lisbeth was the exception to her profession. Her husky voice filled with laughter, blowing away irritation and fear. I was a pale imitation of this born-to-be switchboard operator. Looking back, I now understand the frustration of so many French clients at the time, who, when calling head office were greeted by the incoherent ramblings of an English woman with the vocabulary of a five-year-old.

The following is a typical conversation:

Me: Brown and McLane Software Solutions, Bonjour.

Client: Monsieur de Vries à l'appareil.

Me: [In bad French] You want to speak to Mr de Vries [looking frantically at my list of extension numbers and wondering how this is spelt].

Client: [In perfect French] No, I *am* Monsieur de Vries.

Me: Oh, sorry, right.

[Silence, at which point I realised that Mr de Vries was such an important client that I was expected to not only know the name of his company, but the name of the person to whom he wished to speak.]

Client: [In exasperation] Francis de Serves, *s'il vous plait*.

Me: [Following my training instructions and knowing that Monsieur de Serves was the revered Managing Director] Can I have the name of your company, please?

Client: Schlumberger

Me: Sorry?

Client: Schlumberger [It sounded as if he had sneezed or put in an order at the Hollywood Canteen.]

Me: Slum Burger.

Client: Berger not Burger

Me: Yes, one moment, please. I'm putting you through.

[I was pleased to have learnt this expression in French–
Je vous le passe.]

[Some minutes later]

Me: There is no reply. Can I take a message?

Client: *Vous lui dirai que j'ai appelé, et qu'il me rappelle de toute urgence.*

Me: *Pardon?*

Client: [Loud sighs, repeating original sentence slowly]. You will tell him I rang, and you will ask him to call me back urgently.

Me: Ah, yes. Can I have your number please? [It was bloody hard luck that there wasn't a screen on the switchboard to display numbers.]

Client: [In a fast and furious gabble] *Zero un, quarantesept, quatre-vingt-huit, soixante-seize, quatre-vingt-douze.* [This should have read 01 47 88 76 92]

Me: [Writing] 014074208601642012

Madame Calmelane came to see me later that same afternoon holding out my telephone message. There were a series of crossings out all over the paper. I learnt, slowly and painfully, with much hair loss over the switchboard and several painful outbursts of eczema on my hands, arms and legs, that French numbers needed to be added up to deduce the correct number. If you were French, you did this in your head. If you were me, you did it on a jotter. For a long time, I made the following calculations on my reception notepad.

$4\ 20\ 16 = 4 \times 20 + 16 = 96$

$4\ 20\ 8 = 4 \times 20 + 8 = 88$

It was the only way to keep up with the rapid fire of French thrown at me.

Names were also problematic. I spelt both the name of the company and the caller incorrectly. The kinder sales team members played games in the smoker's lounge, reading out names phonetically, trying to guess who might have called. The not so understanding reported me to Madame Calmelane – when a big commission hung in the balance, not to mention yearly turnover, office patience was tested.

In an overcrowded lift one day, the grumpy woman with the scowl alighted on the 24th floor. She scrunched her face at me like a pit bull terrier, saying to no-one in particular: 'Why should she get the job when there are so many French girls who need work?' I wanted to drop through the bottom of the lift to Minus Three level and land on a toasted cheese sandwich. No-one replied. Most of the staff were kind, but not everyone was prepared to welcome an incompetent English woman with open arms. Hiring me was the most unconventional move Madame Calmelane had ever made.

Yazid, who was crammed in the corner of the lift that day, winked at me, as if to say: 'When you're fired, remember, you still have choices.'

I had joined the company at a time of internal war. Two companies had recently merged into one, and this had resulted in two conflicting factions. The staff list was a veritable Noah's Ark. There were two of everything: two

Managing Directors; two Heads of Human Resources; two Heads of Marketing; and two Heads of Accounts. This caused untold stress, as theoretically anyone's head might roll. Now that I'd been recruited, there were also two receptionists, as Lisbeth had failed to make it into the hallowed ranks of the secretarial pool. There was still resistance because of her poor *orthographe* or spelling. I knew that most of the staff didn't want her to leave reception. If she did, they'd be left with *me* and company profits might plummet.

Throughout my working day, I came to recognise that the lift up to the 31st floor was a microcosm of French society. It was here that I learnt the useful French expression: *les absents ont toujours tort* (those who are absent, are always wrong), observing my colleagues' tendency to bad-mouth anyone who had recently vacated the group. I noticed how the behaviour of my French female colleagues *changed* whenever they were in the presence of a man, as the women adopted a girlish tone and skittish manner. Hair was tossed, and eyes encouraged to peep from beneath fringes in that coy Lady Diana manner, as creatures of my sex feigned subservience in both gesture and in speech. These women would show great respect to a male colleague when wishing him *bonjour, au revoir* or *bon appétit*. But it was gloves off once *monsieur* had gone.

'*C'est un vrai con celui-là.*' He's a right bastard that one. '*Oui, et en plus, il se tape sa secrétaire!*' Yes, and on top of that, he's screwing his secretary.

Femininity evaporated from the huddled group as they picked at the bones of the absent male. Voices grew guttural, descending a register to their natural level. The company of men, I now knew, required stage presence. Never more so than with *un cadre*. A flighty and feminine manner was *de rigueur* in the presence of any male member of staff but once alone, the women reverted to type.

Simone de Beauvoir described such transformations in her book *The Second Sex*, where she described having left her girlfriend one afternoon, her friend's hair unwashed, her clothing drab, and her skin as grey as a school dishcloth, only to pop back later to find the same girl glowing and transformed beyond recognition as she flung the door open in anticipation of her lover. Of course, lovers the world over pamper themselves before a date, but it was at the office where I first noticed that French women changed their *personality* in the presence of the opposite sex. It was the same on the radio and television, where they acted *silly* for the benefit of a man: orgasmic over a new washing powder or a cut-price bargain at the supermarket, they oozed sexuality in their ads, whimpering and gushing to anyone who might listen. In adverts featuring offices, the woman would invariably play the sexy stern secretarial type in the heavy-framed glasses, waiting for a man to unwrap her, and reveal her true passionate self.

I cringed to observe how women would whip themselves into a frenzy on French radio over banal and uninteresting domestic issues: '*Chéri! C'est incroyable!* Carrefour supermarket has a promotion on sirloin steak, two for the price of one. Oh, my love, you could be in for a treat tonight!'

It was an act, a pretence and a conspiracy, in which all French women were happy to collude. In real life, when the whimpering and gushing stopped, the voices of these wives and mothers were deep and authoritative. They were in full control of their emotions, their husbands and their children. The married women that *I* knew were rulers of the roost, governing their households with the authority of Bonne-Maman, their husbands falling in with the arrangement and obeying their spouses iron command. Women ruled and dominated the family home. Men sought revenge at the office.

When first shopping at the butcher's shop for Florence I'd been shocked by the noticeable lack of pleases and thankyous, used by a French woman when giving orders. No, *pleasemayIhavesomeham*, but an authoritative, *you will cut me two slices of ham*, and a reminder once again, that the French were more compliant when instilled with the fear of god, than when someone was *too* 'nice'. French women were naturally competitive with other women. Seven years at an all-girls' comprehensive school had taught me to value close female friendships. We did not consider the boys at the school across the road to be any better than we were. There was no need to make *concessions*. In our radical single-sex school, close and intimate relationships with other girls were paramount, along with the belief that we were not only equal but perhaps *superior*. We could have children, run the home and become nuclear physicists … or poets. There was none of the obsequious bowing and scraping I'd seen in the French office lift. Women were invariably our best friends since there were no men to be friends with. Like many other girls in my class, I had shed genuine tears of sorrow when dumped by a girlfriend who had chosen another soulmate over me, experiencing as much pain in these break-ups as with any boyfriend in later years. It was new for me to be in a society where men commanded all the attention, and where women fawned and minced until they had caught their prey and carried it home to bludgeon into shape.

When French women weren't cooing in the lift, there was of course the usual back-stabbing that I'd known when growing up. I knew everyone bitched the world over. But there had been a sense back home that an inner circle of friends was sacred. It was not so at the office, where anyone was a fair target and it seemed no one was safe.

'*Elle a grossi.*' She has grown fat.

'*T'as vu ce qu'elle porte?*' Have you seen what she's wearing?

'*Son mec l'a plaquée.*' Her bloke dumped her! '*Tu m'étonnes!*' Are you surprised?

'*Je ne la supporte pas!*' I can't stand her!

I hadn't yet seen evidence of the kind of love and loyalty between the women that my friends at school had shared, but then I was no longer at school. One day I would form close friendships with French women, and I would learn that although it might take longer to get there, when you did, it was for life. There *was* an inner circle, but to be in it, you had to belong. For the time being, I needed to be patient.

Madame Calmelane, who kept to herself, was a natural giver of orders and was respected, albeit feared, by her employees. In this way, she resembled my old head teacher. I was one of the few members of staff to like and respect her; grateful to this woman who at a comfortable point in her career had taken a risk in hiring me. I admired her strength and intelligence and understood why she should keep her distance from other members of staff. Lisbeth, like many of my other colleagues, was quick to criticise our boss, though hanging on to her every word and mooning all over her at reception whenever she thought there might be a chance of an upgrade in position.

Lisbeth told me that she preferred the *other* Head of Human Resources (of course there were two) an exotic woman from the Middle-East named Isra. She was mindblowingly beautiful. She floated into the office late each day wearing bright red lipstick and clothes which were the fabric of dreams. She had huge doe-like eyes, laden with mascara, clear olive skin and long wavy dark hair. She was a smoker, along with 90 per cent of all the other women in the office, and drifted past reception every five minutes to ask if I had missed any of her calls – or misunderstood them. Madame Calmelane was in the process of eliminating Isra from the company and had taken away all her duties, so that she *had* no incoming calls of any importance. And yet the switchboard never stopped bleating in her honour. All of the callers were men. One of her callers was a man with a deep voice and an officious manner, who asked if Isra was available about forty times a day. He was exhausting in his demands, and monopolised the switchboard to the extent that I was convinced at first that he must be our biggest client. He hadn't bought a multi-million-dollar software programme. He was Isra's lover. One of her many admirers. I signed for the bunches of red roses and bottles of champagne which arrived daily. Seizing the opportunity to take a quick peek into her office, I spied a fairytale land where it was eternally Valentine's day. In her midthirties with grace, ease and a natural *savoir faire* with men, Isra was the very symbol of French femininity to which I aspired.

Blandine Calmelane, who was in her early fifties, was also attractive and well dressed. I wondered if it was galling for her to be faced with this nubile competitor, and to witness Isra's suitors hunting her down during office hours with such ardour, this exotic second in command snapping at her heels for the job of top dog. Madame Calmelane's marriage had ended in divorce and she was, so the office gossip said, still single. If this bothered her, then she never showed it, continuing to rule her employees with the firm hand of an indulgent headmistress; smart, elegant and gracious. Looking back, I would always be grateful to this woman for having given me a chance to prove myself.

After a few weeks on reception, I was called into a private office and introduced to a man named Richard Grey. He had been drafted in by Madame Calmelane to help ease the rift in the company caused by the merger. In vulgar parlance, he was a 'troubleshooter', who had been hired to eliminate one out of two of all Noah's animals. We couldn't all stay on the Ark. No company, not even an American software company, could justify the expense of two staff members for every post or tolerate half of the entire company blanking the other and barking conflicting orders to new arrivals like me. Richard was an Oxford graduate who was close to retirement. He had set up a consultancy firm in Paris, and integrated companies for several weeks at a time, a clandestine spy, whispering to Madame Calmelane on a daily basis who she should keep and who she should fire. All members of staff were invited to talk to Richard, including me. I warmed to him immediately.

As I was called into the room I felt as if I'd been asked to step into the study of an Oxford professor. Richard was an ex-diplomat, an attractive man who held himself well and bore the vestiges of that Classical education and promise that he had drowned in the amber dregs of a whisky glass over the years. The exact office he had held at the Foreign Office was hazy in detail, but it was all 'hush hush' stuff out in the Middle-East: 'Embassy business'; the furtive 'tap on the nose and wink to the wise' kind of posting. Richard was dressed in a shabby tweed jacket and trousers, with sensible brogues. His manner was bumbling but his mind laser sharp – perfect for a potential ex-spy/diplomat. Sharp in the mornings, that is. After midday it was hit and miss, with Richard opening a bottle of whisky each morning and sipping from breakfast onwards.

Richard had read Ancient Greek and Latin and spoke French, Italian, Russian and German fluently. How many of his stories were true is debatable. It didn't matter. He was one of those great *raconteurs* for whom truth should never get in the way of a good story.

'There was this time when I had to get girls out of Saudi, you understand. Little fools thought they'd married for love, and found themselves married to men who reverted to radical Islam before the bloody plane was halfway across Europe. Most were pregnant or had young children who we had to smuggle out. We weren't allowed to go through the official channels, you understand, but something had to be done. I'd have an unmarked car and tell them to be at a certain street corner at a certain time. We'd bundle them in the boot and get them over the border and home. Night-time operations, of course.'

Richard had grown up in London near Pinewood Studios, and told me how, in 1951, he had met Audrey Hepburn outside the studios on the day of her screen audition for *Roman Holiday*. He claimed he had fallen in love on sight and taken her out to tea.

'The most beautiful young girl I would ever see.' I wanted the story to be true.

On my first meeting with Richard he looked me up and down and told me that I should make more of an effort to dress stylishly. Jessica had found a temping job by then and had reclaimed her white blouse, black skirt and shoes. We were still in the thrall of a secret organisation, living on a diet of Chinese dumplings, and waiting to save up enough money to find a new place to live. I'd reverted to wearing my baggy student clothes from Aber. They were more suited for Glastonbury than the upper echelons of La Tour Washington.

I mentioned in passing that of course I'd like to dress better, but money was still tight until my first wages at the end of the month. Richard noted this on a piece of paper in cramped letters, and I thought no more of it, until two days later, Madame Calmelane arrived at reception before lunch and told me that we were going shopping. My boss marched me to the Les Quatre Temps shopping centre, and to one of those swish shiny shops with slippery floors, where there weren't any price tags in the windows. The window showed a minimalistic display of tight-fitting suits in bright colours; clothes that required accessories shoes, scarves, belts and hats *à la* Audrey Hepburn.

Madame Calmelane asked me to choose two suits and sat in the changing room while I tried on several options, stepping out of the changing room for her approval. *Pretty Woman* had just been released and I felt like Julia Roberts in the posh shop. Eventually I settled on a bright cherry-red jacket and skirt, and an electric-blue suit. They were perfect fare for a receptionist: classical and elegant. I wondered how long they would stay clean, as we didn't have a washing machine, nor did I own any other shoes than a pair of flat ones, which were too clunky for such an outfit. I'd have to fund the extras myself.

Back at the office I changed in the toilets. Richard

was back that afternoon to see Madame Calmelane and winked as he passed through reception. At around half past four, he escorted Madame Calmelane out of the office, his arm linked in hers. She threw her head back laughing, resting it on his shoulder, skittish as a teenager and as beautiful as I realised she must once have been. Later Richard told me that he had made love to her that day, though soon afterwards she was forced to dismiss him for being drunk at work.

One night when Jessica and I were asleep in our fold-up camp beds we were woken by the sound of banging on the stairs outside. Since we had not seen a living soul in the apartment opposite since the day we moved in, and the only person to come up to our segment of the landing was our benefactor Magwitch, I wondered if he had come to finish us off.

'You hear that?' Jessica whispered. 'What do we do?'

'Keep quiet!'

We lay in terror for over an hour, imagining trained assassins dismantling the staircase or building a wall to block us inside.

'Maybe the guy opposite is back?' I said hopefully. 'Maybe he's moving out?'

'It's three in the morning!'

Sometime before dawn the noises stopped and I fell into an uneasy sleep. We barely had time to speak that morning as we were both late for our respective jobs in the city. Jessica was working as a temp in the upmarket

Place Vendome, at a prestigious law firm not too far from the Ritz. She told me how at lunchtimes she would walk to the rue de Rivoli and buy herself a newspaper or a book from WH Smith's, crossing over to the Jardin des Tuileries to sit by one of the ornamental lakes to read it.

Jessica had that knack of making her experience of Paris sound more authentic than my own. It didn't help that she worked in the historical heart of Paris, a stone's throw from the Louvre, whereas I was in the business centre that had sprung up comparatively recently. I could have been in any big city in the world, whereas *she* could only have been in Paris. I ate in a canteen with a conveyor belt of trays and a smell of disinfectant and old mop heads reminiscent of school, whereas Jessica ate onion soup with a glass of house red in one of the local brasseries around the Musée du Louvre. Like Richard, my flatmate was a fantastic storyteller, and I begged her for a second rendition of some of my favourite tales of her adventures *au bureau*.

She worked under the auspices of an individual she labelled 'a budding Axel Blanchard' – a serious looking young man with dark hair and oversized glasses, named Dominique Fromentin. *Utterly bourgeois*, she moaned in pleasure.

Just as I had believed in Jessica's improbable stories of love and seduction, re-enacted back in the school toilets, so she enthralled me now with stories of Paris, and of Dominique Fromentin, her enticing new boss – nothing more than an Axel Blanchard underling – who would grow to love her, slowly but surely, and in absolute defiance of his Avenue Hoch type family. Jessica wasn't above casting herself in the story as the strict and overly repressed English secretary. From her bag of props she produced the oversized pair of black spectacles for which her sharp-sighted, pale-blue eyes had no need, but which she wore to work each day, in order to indulge in a little fantasy that she might whip Vincent's backside with a rolled-up copy of *Le Monde*. Or vice versa if she made any more grammatical errors in his copy. There were multiple incidents to relate when she came home: looks and twinkles by the Xerox machine, or brushed fingertips when clumsily keying in the number of a fax. Most of it was made up for my benefit. Jessica loved an audience. I knew deep down she was a staunch feminist who could chew Dominique Fromentin to pieces and spit out the gristle if she chose, but she saw life as a stage-set on which to perform, regaling me with her preposterous tales as we sipped *Potage Pekinois* from Styrofoam bowls.

Without the funds for a trip to the theatre or cinema which we both so loved, we made our own entertainment.

Evenings were spent at home in the flat, hiding from Magwitch and watching Jessica perform. We had grown used to the usual bag of Chinese dumplings waiting for us on the door handle. We took it for granted now but remembering the thuds and bangs in the middle of the previous night, and our terror, I wondered how much longer this situation could last.

Jessica got back half an hour later than me, and was just about to launch into a tale of how Dominique had punished her 'by not letting her go out for her lunch and making her stay behind after the other girls had left' story, when there was a loud banging at the door.

'Magwitch!'

'I didn't hear the boots.'

Our benefactor still wore his dapper high-heels.

'Je sais que vous êtes là.'

It was a man's voice, but not one that we knew. *'Ouvrez! Je sais que vous êtes là-dedans!'*

And then in perfect English: 'Open the bloody door, will you?'

I felt we had no choice but to obey. On the doorstep was an attractive man, who I was relieved to see was not proffering a bag of Chinese food. He had waves of dark hair which would have been described in a romantic novel as *tousled*, and was dressed in a smart suede jacket and jeans, the sort that would have given Bryan Ferry a run for his money. In other words, attractive, but not so much *pouty* as foul-tempered. The man pushed passed us.

'Excuse me,' Jessica said in her haughty voice, forgetting to attempt French in her fury, 'you can't just barge in here. This is our flat.'

'Actually,' the man replied, in perfect English, 'I think you'll find it's *my* flat. As is the apartment opposite. Or what's left of it!'

'What do you mean?'

'Did you two not hear anything suspicious in the night?'

Jessica and I looked at one another with a guilty expression.

'We sleep at night,' she said primly, 'and we keep our door locked.'

'Why?' I asked.

'I've been cleaned out,' the man said. 'Every bit of furniture. Whoever took it knew they would not be disturbed. You cannot tell me you did not hear, *n'est-ce pas*? They even took the partner's desk that belonged to my father. This was so heavy it would have needed five men to carry it away!'

'Well, there was a *bit* of bumping' I said. 'I'm really sorry, but we've been having some ... unwanted visitors. People troubling us. And we didn't want to open the door in case it was them.'

'Chinese, I suppose!'

The man strode across the room and threw open the balcony door. He leant outside and lit a cigarette. The wind ruffled his hair which was just starting to streak grey. He was tanned, and I realised that this must be Henri Martin, the elusive journalist whose name we had seen inscribed on the door opposite.

'What do you mean this is *your* flat?' Jessica asked. I knew she was wondering if we owed this man rental money.

'I own both flats,' he said. 'I travel all over the world. I'm never here. I've been out reporting in the desert, and I've come home to find that my apartment has been turned over. Not only that, but this place, which the agency assured me had been let to "a highly paid insurance broker," a *cadre*, is in fact let to two ...' he hesitated, seeking the right word, 'to the two of *you*, who it appears do not own one stick of furniture. What is *this*?'

He pointed to a small pile of debris on the floor in

the middle of the room: the remnants of baguette and Babybel cheese wrappers, the empty wine bottle and cartons of takeaway food from Magwitch. A dragon's lair that had formed over the past week, dried orange peel sprinkled like confetti across the floor.

'We are professional women who work in Paris, with serious jobs,' Jessica said firmly, toeing a dirty sock under her camp bed. 'I have a placement with a top law firm on the rue de Rivoli, and my friend works for a top American company; a software company selling millions of dollars of – erm, soft things.'

'Really? And you for instance – how long have you been in employment?'

'A week.'

Henri Martin made a *pfff* noise. It was a noise that only the French could get away with. It signified utter disgust and was as much about the lip and head gestures as the word itself.

'The agency is meant to inspect my tenants. I ask for three-years' employment on a permanent contract. Are you on permanent contracts?'

'Not yet.'

We were both on a trial run. Henri Martin hurled his cigarette over the balcony like a cricket ball. I had the feeling he'd like to throw us both over after it.

'I have been tricked,' he said. 'You are stupid girls. *Des imbéciles. Des idiotes.* The agency has dealings with the Chinese criminal world. I have a friend who has been investigating. He told me to come home and see what was happening. Because they know we are investigating them – this (he pointed in the direction of his empty flat) is my "thank you gift", along with you two useless individuals. I have not had any rent yet. The deposit you were supposed to pay, where is that? You at least had the decency to pay this, I suppose?'

We hung our heads.

'So,' he laughed. 'I am housing you rent-free, without even a lump sum to pay for any damages.'

'We don't have much, but we are honest,' I said.

Henri Martin looked around the room which was empty bar the two camp beds and an upturned wooden crate, which we were using both as a table and a chair – a multifunctional object in our lives.

'Then it will not take you long to move,' he said. 'I will be back tomorrow evening. I must go to the hotel now, since I no longer have a bed to sleep in. I will meet you here at eight. And you must be packed. I will expect my rent.'

Henri Martin's visit threw Jessica into a panic. I had never seen her in such a state. She began to throw her clothes haphazardly into her suitcase, swiping her shampoo and make-up from the bathroom.

'Don't go,' I said. 'We'll find a new flat. We both have jobs now.'

She wouldn't listen. She went out into Paris without her coat and returned to tell me that she had found a Euro-lines coach home to Manchester. It was a journey lasting over twenty hours but it was cheap and would take her north. Our world had crumbled. The only thing she wanted to do was bolt. For good this time. She left from La Place de la République at eleven o'clock that night.

'So, this is goodbye,' I said. 'What about your bed?' 'Keep it,' she said. 'I want nothing of this life.'

The difference between us was that Jessica had a home to go back to. Her old bedroom, painted black in the early days of her conversion to existentialism, was still there, waiting for her. I knew there wasn't a safehouse waiting for me across The Channel, but thought I'd try anyway. I went to a local phone box and called my dad. Although I didn't know it, he'd met someone and was also in the process of leaving home.

'Can I come back?'

'Your mum won't like that. We sold your bed.' 'You keep telling me.'

'You don't wanna come home, kid. There'd only be arguments. What the hell do you wanna come back for? You've got yourself a job now, and you'll have far more fun in Paris than you will stuck back here. I'll send you some money to tide you over till you get your first wages.'

'All right. Thanks.' 'Bye, kid.'

'Bye, Dad.'

CHAPTER 20

Jessica left the flat around nine that evening, loaded up like a packhorse. I had a visit from Henri Martin to look forward to. He arrived on the dot, walked in and began pacing the room like a panther. He spotted immediately that we were one tenant down.

'Friend gone?'

I nodded, dreading the next question which I knew would be about money and deposits. He gave a contemptuous snort.

'Come with me.'

I followed him out of the flat and to the end of the corridor to a door which I hadn't noticed before. We climbed some stairs and pushed through a fire escape, coming out onto the roof top. Perhaps he wanted to push me to my death.

There was a small terrace area which overlooked the city towards the Parc de la Villette. I could see the futuristic statues in metal over the slate rooftops of the building opposite. Henri lit a cigarette and leant on the railings. I noticed that there was a small wrought-iron chair in the corner and a collection of cigarette stubs. I wondered how often he came up here. If we had known of this escape route, Jessica and I might have been able to hide from Magwitch and have our picnic dinners up here with the pigeons. It was sad Jessica wasn't here to share this moment and I felt a pang of sorrow that our adventures together were over.

'I love this view,' Henri said. 'Sometimes I come up here and write when I'm home.'

'What do you write?'

'Oh, stuff for work; news articles about the war, political articles. Poems sometimes, and the start of a novel. I might pack it all in one day, stay here and write books.'

'That's what I want to do. But I don't feel I've lived enough yet.'

'I'm guessing you don't have my money.' 'No. Sorry.'

'No surprise there then. Well, it looks as though I'm going to have to put this one down to experience.'

'I can pay you back, when I get my wages.'

He laughed. 'I've a whole house full of goods to replace. Let's hope the insurance people are kind. I put it down to good karma. Maybe if I'm good to you, they'll be good to me. But you have to leave the flat. I'll give you three days.'

'*Merci beaucoup.*'

He looked at me seriously now.

'Oh, and one piece of advice. Don't tell those bastards where you're going.'

I didn't see Henri again. I liked him and sensed a twinge of regret. I could easily have developed a crush on this philosophic man of letters. He looked like someone who should have been raiding lost arks; a man who, like Icarus, was drawn to danger; someone with stories to tell, and lines of fatigue around his eyes that I fancied were the vestiges of experiences in war-torn countries across the world. It was childish to romanticise. I was no better than Jessica with her precious Dominique Fromentin. I respected the fact that although I was in his debt Henri did not try to take advantage of the situation, while at the same time regretting the fact he didn't once try. I knew that for Henri Martin, I was nothing more than a silly English girl who couldn't pay her rent.

Back at the office I confided in Madame Calmelane that I was being evicted. She sent me to see her second-in-command, a woman called Henriette Fresnel, who was responsible for staff social welfare. Henriette told me that I had the same chin and smile as Jane Birkin, the English actress who had married Gainsbourg, and spent most of the meeting staring at me. Henriette was kind, with muscly legs and an athletic figure. She reminded me of our sports teacher at school; one of those no-frills kind of women who only wore skirts under duress and was happiest in a tracksuit jogging round the park.

Henriette put my name on a waiting list for an HLM studio flat. HLM buildings were the equivalent of low rental council flats. The company had a wide reach and could prioritise rentals for its staff. There wasn't anywhere available but Henriette had a solution.

'I have spoken to Lisbeth,' she said. 'She is happy to let you stay in her house in Bezons until we find something. Do you have any objection?'

'No, of course not,' I said, 'if Lisbeth doesn't mind.'

'She will be glad of the rent,' said Henriette, 'though it's only temporary.'

I wondered aloud how I was going to get my stuff out of the flat. It would be awful to run into Magwitch now that Jessica had gone. Henriette made a quick phone call and arranged for a kindly salesman with a van to come and help me that evening at six. The company certainly took excellent care of its staff. Six o'clock was prime time for Magwitch visits, but this was not something I could explain to Henriette. I tried to change the time with the man with the van, but to no avail. He couldn't do it any later, as he had a wife and family to get home to. I hoped that we could clear out before my 'gentleman' caller arrived – if he dared to come back – having organised the stripping of Henri Martin's flat. I sensed it would take more than this to dissuade him. When we arrived, my colleague, whose name was Bernard, a kindly plodding man with bulbous eyes who wouldn't be rushed, waited patiently for a space and carefully parked the van outside the apartment door, his warning lights flashing.

'Will this take long?' he asked.

'No. I've packed my bags, there's only a camp bed which needs to come down, if you could manage that.'

I'd have to leave Jessica's bed there. Like Melville's Bartleby the Scrivener, the only trace of her that remained was a slight indentation in the sheets.

'Not a problem.'

My heart raced as we opened the door to the flat. The door-handle was devoid of its customary food parcel. Our benefactor hadn't graced us with his presence yet. I ran around, scooping up my belongings and stuffing things into carrier bags. We made a first trip to the van and then returned for the camp bed. As Bernard slammed the van door shut I jumped so hard I practically landed on the roof-top terrace. Behind the van door was Magwitch in all his glory, same black-heeled boots, a pair of tight black trousers and a shiny silk shirt badly buttoned, to reveal his protruding stomach. He smiled as if we were the oldest of friends and shook hands with Bernard like a benevolent parent whose daughter was going on a date.

'Going out?' he asked. 'Yes, I'm leaving.'

'And the other girl – the dark-haired one – she is gone?'
'Yes. Back to England. For good.'

He shrugged.

'*Je vois*. Well, I need new address, to forward letters if they come. A few more matters to discuss together, I think, but I see you busy. But we meet again. Soon, yes?' 'I don't remember the address right now,' I said, which was true.

'I wait – and you search. Yes?'

Bernard smiled and patted the man on the shoulder. 'I have it,' he said. 'Just a minute.'

My heart sank. Bernard had unwittingly signed over one of my fingers, if not two. Maybe he'd take an extra one for Jessica, seeing as she wasn't here. My well-meaning colleague took out a pen and paper from his pocket and pressing the biro firmly into the paper as he methodically inscribed the letters. He pushed the paper into Magwitch's hand. Magwitch looked, smiled and pocketed it.

'Until we meet again,' he said, and tripped off with a tip-tap, like the troll on the Billy Goat's Bridge. Bernard registered my look of horror.

'*Allez, montez*,' he said, and held open the door of the van so that I could climb in.

We set off. I wanted to hurl the contents of my stomach out of the car window.

'Don't worry,' Bernard said, as we got going. 'I gave him the address of my ex-mother-in-law. She's a complete bitch. Let her deal with him.'

'You didn't give him Lisbeth's address?' 'Do I look stupid?'

'Thank fuck for that!'

I sank back into the plush leather seat. Free at last.

Lisbeth lived with her father in a small house under the Bezons bridge. It was a temporary measure, while she waited for the large three-bedroom HLM (or council) flat Human Resources had promised her. Her father wasn't there; something to do with a new woman. The house was ramshackle, and the cars shook the foundations as they whooshed up on the overhead bypass. There was a miniscule kitchen in the original hallway, bleeding into a living room, off which there was a single bedroom where I'd be setting up my camp bed. Lisbeth had a double bedroom on the first floor above mine with a small balcony.

She let me into a secret almost as soon as I'd heaved my last bag through the door.

'Extension 111,' she said, 'have you seen him?' 'I don't remember. What's his name?'

We often referred to employees by their extension number.

'Rocheran, Charles-Henri.' 'Why?'

Lisbeth winked. 'One day, now we live together, I'll tell you,' she said with a heavy mascara wink.

The following week, a group of managers came out of a conference room and shook hands with their clients in the reception area. There was much laughter and false guffawing. A man with salt and pepper hair and round owlish glasses was centre of the group. Lisbeth nudged me and reddened.

'That's him!' she hissed. 'Extension 111.' '*Et alors?*'

'I'm dating him. But you can't tell anyone. He's a *cadre*, you see.'

In between the shrill shriek of the switchboard and the hundred repetitions of '*Good morning, can you hold the line please*,' Lisbeth explained to me that Madame Calmelane and the rest of staff would disapprove of her relationship because of the difference in status. In other words, Lisbeth wasn't considered worthy enough to be shagged by someone higher up the in-house pyramid of staff members. There wasn't an official ban on relationships between staff members – others had met and married, but not out of *rank*.

'I am not even a *secretary* yet,' she said. 'I'm just on

switchboard. Charles-Henri is Head of Sales. *And* he's married.'

'Isn't *that* the worse part?'

'No! His wife left him, long before we got together. She ran off with another man and abandoned her two children: a boy and a girl. The girl was only six weeks old when she left. She fell in love with another man while she was pregnant.'

Lisbeth smiled, her face lighting up.

'I love the children,' she said. 'They are so adorable. I go to the house to play with them. Charles-Henri lives in Bougival in a *mansion*. He lives next to Gerard Depardieu's wife and son. But he's all alone and sad.'

I looked at the laughing man and thought how ridiculous it was. If Lisbeth made him happy, why should they have to keep their relationship a secret?

I soon settled into Lisbeth's house, with an assurance from Henriette that I wouldn't have to wait long for my own apartment. On our first weekend together Lisbeth got up early to make hot croissants, with jam and butter, fresh from the oven, pouring steaming black coffee into mugs. Warm croissants were something Jessica and I had dreamt of at weekends, as we broke hard lumps of sesame-seed cake together. It was one of those *French* moments that reminded us we were in Paris, like hot onion soup before the cinema, or pancakes with hot frothy chocolate in the Tuileries, while pigeons pecked around our feet.

Lisbeth plugged in a small electric oven and placed

the croissants carefully on the grill. We were busy drying our hair in the other room and putting make-up on by the mirror when a strange smell wafted in, followed by a hideous squeaking. We searched the room but found nothing. It was only when Lisbeth opened the grill that we saw four croissants neatly laid out, and next to the fourth, lined up in perfect symmetry, a dead mouse freshly toasted to death. It was my first experience of mice. Horrified, Lisbeth donned a pair of gloves and disposed of the corpse, insisting we eat the croissants anyway, though the death scene on the grill had spoilt the romance of the moment. She was nervous that morning, checking her watch every five minutes. Charles-Henri was due at the house at any moment.

He arrived late that afternoon, swooping her up into his arms to apologise for the delay. After a few suckerfish movements on the fullness of Lisbeth's lips, Charles-Henri greeted me in a friendly manner quite unlike his usual pompous work manner. I was surprised he didn't mind the full-on kissing with me in the room. As I sat on the small, squashed sofa, he loomed over me at an unfortunate angle to plant a kiss on my cheeks, thrusting a huge erection encased in a pair of tight jeans into my face. Frolicking with a staff member at the lower end of the company's organisational chart had apparently not had a negative effect on the man's libido, and desire bounced from the walls of the tiny room. After much slobbering and pawing, the couple departed for the evening, Lisbeth wrapped around her lover like a seahorse to its mate.

I checked out Lisbeth's wardrobe for a pretty dress. She'd said I could borrow anything I liked. I wanted to look my best tonight. I was off on a 'date' of my own. I'd been invited to visit a barge in the suburbs of Paris where the river Seine flowed into the Oise. It belonged to an Englishman called Jay Allaway who worked on the 24th floor of our office. He was a tall, good-looking man in his late twenties with a crest of shiny jet-black hair and an impressive set of perfect white teeth. He was also a *cadre*. Jay was restoring the barge, which was moored up north where it was much cheaper than any mooring under the shadow of the Eiffel Tower. His project, once the boat was finished, was to give up his flat and live there permanently. Life near the water's edge was something which appealed to my romantic side. I used to fantasise about a house in Cornwall, or life on a barge.

It would be a relief to communicate in English again. Since Jessica's departure my life had been led in pidgin French. My language skills were still cringe-worthy, and at the end of a long day massacring the language, my head ached. There were times when I loathed hearing French, and no more so than when I switched the radio on in the morning. Living in France at this time, meant learning French ... *being* French. There was no choice. I suffered for my language skills. Hair loss and eczema were tiny details in the process. If I could speak French, *anyone* could.

But that night my date with Jay was a welcome opportunity to slip back into English. Even with Lisbeth, whose English was good, I was aware of speaking *slowly* and *clearly* SO THAT SHE WOULD UNDERSTAND

EVERY WORD, avoiding any typically English idioms or expressions.

As Jay drove and the bustling city of lights fellbehind us, we chatted and relaxed to music. He pulled off the main road and headed down towards the riverbank. It was almost dark. We were in a quiet country backwater, the riverbank lined with weeping willows. It was hard to imagine that Paris was only an hour away. We climbed on deck and Jay took out a can of thick black gloss. He lit a small oil-lamp and began to paint. The outside world vanished into a thick blanket of inky darkness far from the shrill beep of the switchboard, the lamplight casting its mellow glow onto Jay's face as he painted. The boat was called *Le Rival*. Concentrated on his brushstrokes, his voice rich and soft, Jay told me that he'd grown up on the boat but that it had been sold on by his father many years ago.

'On this *actual* boat? So, you've been here years then?'

'Yes, with my mother, father and sister. But when my mother died the boat was auctioned off. I wanted a barge to remember her by and started to look for one of my own. One day there was this ad in the paper. I called up and came out here to see her. Of all the boats in the world, she had to sail back into my life. A bit worse for wear, but still *Le Rival*. Even found some of my graffiti on the bunk beds downstairs.'

I was intrigued by the fact that Jay had lived in France for so long. It explained why his French was flawless.

'You went to school here?'

'I didn't go to school after we came to France. Not from

the age of about twelve.'

He took some time to tell me the story, but as night drew in, we moved closer together like moths around the storm lamp, as he told me that his father had been a criminal, on the run from the police in the United Kingdom.

'We fled to France and lived in hiding for years. We never dared ask how or where the money came from, but Dad would disappear and come back with it, in dribs and drabs. Then Mum got sick. She kept it quiet for a long time, knowing that she couldn't go to the doctors, or give her real name. She never got any treatment thanks to that bastard and then she died.'

'What? *Here?*'

'Yes. Here.'

We went below deck and I looked at the narrow galley kitchen and the living room with the wooden bench which ran around three sides of a small table and imagined what it must have been like cooped up in these few square feet with a man on the run and a mother who was suffering, but too scared to seek help.

'He must have done something pretty bad, then?' Jay didn't answer.

'Did you ever see him again?'

He snorted. 'Yes, quite recently in fact! I decided to let bygones be bygones. He tracked me down and came to stay in my flat. Gave a sob story about how sorry he was. We had a meal, drank a lot of wine. He went to bed, and when I woke up in the morning he'd gone and taken all my bank cards with him. Cleaned me out.'

Several hours later, up on deck, we kissed. It felt strange to kiss an English man. All the men to occupy my thoughts in the past year had been French. It felt comfortable, like eating mash with warm butter and HP sauce: homegrown; familiar. It was more romantic than with Steve, but a lot of that was to do with the boat creaking beneath the bows of an old oak, and the stories Jay had told. We drove back to Paris and Jay dropped me off.

'I've got a girlfriend,' he said as I opened the car door. 'She's German. We've been together for ten years, but we don't make love anymore.'

I knew already that this was not meant to be.

Jay and I met several times after work. Our relationship had shifted foot and become more of a friendship, mutual loneliness bringing us together. We clung onto a loose attraction, knowing that neither was right for the other: two foreigners lost in a city where, to the other, each felt like home. We caught the metro into Paris and bought a beer in Chatelet les Halles. Jay let me into a secret. He came home this way to visit the sex shops, not to sleep with women, but to pleasure himself before he went back for the night. It wasn't the kind of secret I thought he would tell me if he intended me to fall in love.

Sickened but somehow curious, I followed him into a shop which sold the usual gimmicks, and where I witnessed the extent of his sadness: the plastic penises, the dressing-up gear, the rows of pornographic videos which, despite their French titles, reminded me of some of the films the rugby set would watch in the TV room back in Ifor Evans Hall of Residence. I remembered how the men used to cram in, and switch the lights off, calling obscenities at the screen. I'd tiptoed in once and pretended not to watch, marvelling at the mechanics of a process of which, at the time, I'd had no experience.

Jay's lonely visits here were bleak and heart-breaking. I asked him how often he visited, and he said perhaps two or three times a week, before going home and lying in bed next to a woman who had no desire to be touched by him. Her name was Kristine. He showed me a photo. She was a stunning blonde peering majestically over a glass of champagne. The sex shops of Chatelet les Halles were infertile places for love to grow. It was a plastic and clinical world of handcuffs and blow-up plastic dolls with garish faces, but Jay wanted to share his after-work haunt. Perhaps he hoped that I'd shock him out of his own sad routine. He had fallen into a world stripped of emotion and couldn't find his way back. His face was white and strained. He'd been more at peace painting the barge as it swayed beneath the willows that moonlit night. I thought of the boy who had taught himself Maths and English, who read books in his bunk bed to educate himself, before finally paying his own way through French business school. He'd done all that, yet he hadn't found love.

At the back of the shop there were three cubicles with black curtains like the changing rooms in Next. We went into one and he sat on the stool. I sat on his knee. This could have been a photo booth and the two of us perched there for a romantic photo. There was a screen in front of us and a slot for coins.

'This is where I watch stuff,' he said.

He didn't feed in the coins. That was a step too far. Beside us, in the armrest, there was an ashtray stuffed to the brim with used tissues. I knew there must be love out there somewhere. We were orphans united in our loneliness, not lovers. There must be more to love in Paris than this.

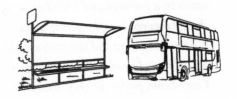

CHAPTER 21

Shortly after Jessica's return to England, she mailed me a letter, addressing me as 'Pig,' her special name for me that harkened back to an old English class when we had decided to incorporate the word *pig* into every Shakespearian text – *Othello* thus becoming Pigello, Hamlet becoming Piglet, and so on.

Dearest Pig,

I am home where I belong. Back in Blighty. I realise now that there is a beauty here in the Cheshire countryside, with its gentle rolling hills, that cannot be matched anywhere else in the world. You can keep your Pyrenees, you can keep Paris. It is not for me. I realise that what I want most of all is what I had all along – England. I want to find my little cottage here. Yes, I'll even grow pink roses around the door and think of you. I realise that everything I want is everything I thought I despised. I don't want to struggle in a foreign language.

Today I drove out with Mum up into the hills and we had

scones in a tearoom and looked at antiques in bow-windowed
shops. I thought how staggeringly beautiful our own countryside
is. I could stay here and discover something new every day of my
life. Why do I need to ever leave again?
Come home, piglet. Blighty always welcomes back its own.
Love or what you will, Jessica x.

Besides the letter, Jessica left me one last parting gift: a blind date. She'd been threatening it for weeks, and now that she had finally departed, it was about to happen. It was one of her colleagues from the law firm on the Place Vendome, and although he was French, his name was William. Despite Jessica's promises that as soon as we set eyes on each other we would hit it off, I was sceptical. Jessica had such strange taste in men that I could not imagine finding anyone she approved of attractive. Later, William told me the same thing.

'Jessica was such a strange girl,' he said. 'I imagined that you would be one of her weird friends. I couldn't believe it when I saw you. *Tu étais si belle.*'

We were both pleasantly surprised. William was a tall, blond man, handsome to say the least. He had a toned body with floppy boyish hair like Antony Andrews in that infamous BBC production of *Brideshead*. He had a French accent with an American twang, having spent two years working in New York and Philadelphia. More recently he'd been temping at the law firm where Jessica worked on the Place Vendome, and was about to start a new permanent job as a trader.

Our first date was at a Chinese restaurant in Paris. I had grown edgy around Chinese food but didn't like to make a fuss. Conversation was *facile* and flowed all night. Afterwards, William drove me home and we kissed in the car outside the house. A woman sang on the radio: 'Come closer, do you want to know a secret, I'm in love with you,' and for the first time since David, my heart felt light and gay. William didn't have a German girlfriend and hadn't suggested we swing by the Chatelet sex clubs on our way home. Things were on the up! We started to date and I was hopeful.

I took William home and introduced him to Lisbeth and Charles-Henri. We met on Friday evenings and spent the weekends together. William had temporarily moved back into his parent's home and I soon learnt that his father, who was a small man like Napoleon, expected to be obeyed in pretty much the same fashion as the military general himself. He would not hear of William using the family home as a hotel, and forbade his only son to use his childhood bedroom without sharing the family meals and eating home each night. This was annoying and frustrating and the only reason we ever argued. William was twenty-six and a full five years older than me. I couldn't imagine living at home and still being told what to do by my parents. William dressed neatly, his shirts carefully ironed by his mum, and radiated the kind of good health which came from three regular meals a day. I was torn between annoyance at the security which cosseted him and a desire to slip into his warm and safe cocoon far from the dangers of the world and to run myself a nice warm bubble-bath back at his place in the suburbs. We'd been to William's family home a few times already, usually when his parents were away, creeping around like intruders in a museum after closing hours.

One Saturday evening around Christmas, William took me into Paris. Despite the cold, I was wearing a silky dress which clung to my body and highlighted the outline of my knickers. William had borrowed his father's glistening Peugeot 605 for the occasion and told me that my outfit would look better without the harsh knicker line. I slipped the offending undergarment off and pushed it under the seat, my head on William's shoulder as he drove down the rue de Rivoli to the Place de La Concorde.

It was nice to see Paris above ground for once. With the loan of William's father's car at the weekend, I had no need for my *carte orange* train pass and had exchanged my daily rodent-style trek through the long interconnecting tunnels of the metro and the RER for the lights of Paris as we zoomed up the Champs Elysées. Paris truly *was* magical, and much deserving of its sobriquet the 'city of lights'. I hadn't much experience of it yet having spent too much time ironing in submarines, trekking to work through tunnels, or on the run.

Surprisingly, although his parents were in residence, William invited me to sleep at the house, so that he could return the car in time for Sunday morning, and we could have lunch with his parents. I was apprehensive, but we arrived home in the early hours of the morning, both tipsy. The Launay family lived in a suburb to the south of Paris in a modern house built in the early 1980s to their design. The address in rue de Nord was as frosty as its name. It was decorated monastically with zero clutter: no books, or ornaments visible. The living room housed a cold leather Chesterfield sofa, a heavy oak dresser polished within an inch of its life and a finger-print-free glass coffee table. The walls were adorned with the kind of pictures found in hotels or impersonal office spaces. The floor tiles gleamed brightly enough to show my drunken reflection.

It was the kind of house certain to show up the slightest smudge; the sort of place where it is easy to put things in the wrong place, to knock over objects from fear, or sully work surfaces; an environment which made me feel as awkward as a giant, life-sized stain myself. Shoes were left in a hallway cupboard along with their coats and jackets. There was a ritual shedding at the entrance hall. I was offered a pair of tartan slippers. My naturally phobic side shied away from wearing other people's slippers – slippers smelt of their owners' feet – but it was this or freeze to death. I chose to freeze. Jessica would have happily donned anyone's cast-off underwear or shoes. Not me.

We crept to the bedroom where I discovered to my amusement that William slept in a polished sleigh bed. I expected Rudolph and his other pals to pull him up through the night sky. The bed smelt of beeswax and the sheets were of the starched and matching variety. There was a dressing-table to one side and a sliding cupboard in which his neatly ironed clothes hung. The family bathroom gleamed with a raised bathtub and symmetrically hung towels. I quivered in excitement. Baths were a luxury since leaving the Blanchard household. The Launay house was as impersonal as a hotel, yet unfortunately we were not alone and could not ring for room service or ask for breakfast in bed. This was not a house where crumbs in beds were authorised.

The only element of fantasy in the whole house was a fox terrier called Rush. His tightly knitted curls clung to his aged head and he skidded to greet me. I was surprised that the family didn't keep this bundle of joy outside. Time and again I learnt that the French did not have the same sentimental attitude to animals. Dogs were often left tied up outside or in a sad garden kennel. Happily for Rush he was allowed inside with the other members of the family, though I was surprised to see that he wasn't wearing slippers. I suspected his paws were wiped down before he was allowed onto the clean floor tiles.

William and I fell into bed and made muted love. The general sparseness of the house encouraged sounds to reverberate (Monsieur Launay *père* snored and snorted so loudly I wondered if he might be under the sleigh bed). Being with William felt far more natural than my kiss with Jay and I was beginning to wonder if, physically at least, I would ever feel at ease with an English boyfriend again. Not that I'd ever made love with an Englishman, since Steve was Welsh.

Next morning, we woke late. There was some confusion as to how quickly we could shovel breakfast in before it was time for lunch. French meals are served on time with military precision, and William's mum had been clattering pans around in the kitchen for several hours, the parents having dutifully respected the breakfasting hour and had their coffee and croissants four hours earlier, having showered and dressed at the crack of dawn and shot to the bakers for bread before ten.

A meaty smell wafted down the gleaming hallway and crept beneath the bedroom door. Not for the first time in my life I marvelled at the superhuman effort it took to be a traditional French wife. Not only did Madame Launay run her home to five-star standards of cleanliness, she held down a serious job as an accountant and provided regular home-made meals. She made jam with plums and apricots sent down from the family farm in Normandy for breakfast and laid fine slithers of apple on home-rolled pastry for dessert. Like most French husbands, Monsieur Launay had never touched an iron or an oven in his life, and yet was quite happy to complain if his food was not on the table in time or prepared to his liking. ('This broccoli is too cooked. The cauliflower is underdone. The meat appears a little dry?') If I had to be re-incarnated as a man, I'd choose to be French every time.

William was tense and anxious that we were out of synch with the family routine, his parents' displeasure tangible at fifty paces.

'We have to get up. My dad doesn't like late risers.'

I sneaked into the bathroom, determined to make use of the pile of fluffy towels and have a good soak.

There was a jar of bath salts on the side and I helped myself liberally. The last few lean months had taught me to make the most of what was available. There was something about knowing that this grumpy French father was waiting that made me want to take my time. Being a Gemini, I sensed that recalcitrant, devilish twin on my shoulder, whispering to its angelic partner: 'Go on, take your time. You work so hard all week. You deserve a little "me time."'

After half an hour of soaking William knocked on the bathroom door to tell me that lunch was ready. I quickly tried to put some order back into the bathroom. It is a truth universally acknowledged that in a tidy house you always make more mess than if you'd *tried* to wreak havoc. There were puddles on the floor where I'd forgotten to place the bathmat, my crumbling blusher had made a powdery mess on the side, and as I tried to guess which toothbrush might be William's so I could clean my teeth, I knocked over a jar of cotton-wool buds. The air was as steamy as a Turkish bathhouse. I pulled on my crumpled dress, but I couldn't find my knickers. Never mind. No-one would know.

William's parents, whose names were Claudine and Jacques, a confusing element since I had abbreviated these names to Claude and Jack in my head and could no longer remember who was who. My first impression on arriving in the dining room, was that the parents had been waiting a long time. They were seated bolt upright on uncomfortable looking chairs with backs as straight as rulers. No-one spoke. Jacques looked at his watch and muttered something under his breath. There was an awkward silence. I couldn't imagine sitting so formally *à table* with my own parents. In the middle of the table there was a collection of glasses and I was offered a choice of sherry, port, or some sickly-looking mixture that smelt of oranges. I had managed to miss breakfast and didn't feel like a morning tipple (although by now it was close to one o'clock in the afternoon). I plumped for the port, smiled and held out my glass, fighting back a rising sense of nausea.

Jacques filled my glass, wiping a stray drip carefully with his paper napkin. There was a small bowl of peanuts in the middle of the table, and a second bowl of Pringles which lay together neatly as if each had been dusted and then replaced symmetrically. Claudine passed round the bowl of Pringles and we crunched silently. Mine crumbled into smithereens between nervous fingers, and I tried to push the pieces under my plate.

As if remembering something, Jacques jumped to his feet, saying something I didn't understand. Neither of William's parents could speak English, which made the choice of their son's christian name bizarre when 'Guillaume' would have been a more obvious choice. William turned to me looking puzzled. 'He says he has found something of yours in the car.' I couldn't think what I might have left in the neatly hoovered car. My *carte orange* perhaps?

Jacques reappeared holding a silky object out warily as if it might bite. I recognised my pink French knickers on sight, specially purchased before my trip to Paris from M&S in the hope of seducing my one-time

Jewish boyfriend. They were typically English, William had told me, French girls preferring snazzy little undergarments the width of a piece of string. Popular in the late 1980s (in Aberystwyth at least), my oversized bloomers would have fit an elephant, but I was fond of them, as they were soft to the touch and, I fancied, with their scalloped edges, rather fetching.

Jacques wafted towards me holding the offending article. He wasn't even trying to find the funny side, his face white with anger as if a dozen leeches had sucked him dry.

'*Vous avez oublié ceci,*' he said.

There was emphasis on the word *these*. You have forgotten *these*. He dangled the knickers over the aperitif glasses like a plague-infested *mouchoir*. William reached up and swiped them from his hand, rolling the offending knickers up into a ball, stuffing them into his pocket like a hanky.

'*Je suis une sans culotte,*' I said, remembering the word from my A level history lessons. No-one so much as smirked, least of all William. I thought the French were meant to be liberal what with all that *Last Tango in Paris*, and *Emmanuelle* sitting naked on her wicker chair back in the seventies. Surely one pair of pink panties wasn't *une affaire d'état!*

I was frustrated that the knickers implied a far more sinful night in the Peugeot than we had had. My unfortunate undergarment must have given rise to fears about smudges of a different kind on the brushed upholstery. I wanted to explain (in French) that the whole issue was not about 'shagging' in the family motor but the removal of an offending knicker line – but those words were impossible to formulate with a hangover, so I gave up.

Claudine cleared the glasses and the bowls. I felt I should help but didn't. Men remained seated in France, whereas women were genetically programmed to jump up before they'd finished their food to prepare the next course without once considering their own personal comfort. I reckoned I'd burnt my bridges whether I moved or not, so I stayed seated. Besides, now they knew I wasn't wearing any knickers, having arrived without an overnight bag, I didn't want to move around the room. Whatever happened I would forever be the English girl who had whipped off her undies in the car.

Besides, I wanted to throw up. Alcohol and Pringles on an empty stomach. And that *smell!* What was it? Claudine returned with a steaming platter of meat. It was not an odour that I recognised.

'Veal,' William said, 'recently slaughtered from the family farm in Normandy.'

Baby calves swimming in blood and curdled-looking cream wasn't on my wish list at the best of times, but I swallowed, held out my plate and smiled.

Etiquette counts for a lot in France and I knew this family were far more likely to forgive the shedding of my underwear than my vomiting *à table*.

My life with William developed a pattern that winter. We met on Friday evenings, after his long week hibernating in the suburbs with his parents. Before our rendez-vous, I changed hurriedly in the office toilets, slipping into a skimpy dress that I had purchased from *Galeries Lafayette* especially for the occasion. William liked feminine clothes; stockings, silky dresses and revealing tops. I was happy to indulge. During the week, I continued to alternate my blue and red work suits, earning myself large pleased smiles from Madame Calmelane as she passed reception, and *petit à petit* my French began to improve.

I followed the advice my old friend Richard had given me, binning the baggy clothes and beginning to dress less like a hippy student from Aberystwyth and more like a French girl. During the week, I joined work colleagues at the downstairs bar or in town. I had become the best of friends with a black-American man from Atlanta who had joined the office, sending tidal waves rippling throughout the whole organisation. His name was Ronald McKenzie and he was Head of Human Resources Europe, which gave him direct authority over Madame Calmelane. Ron was nothing if not controversial in the office, as his presence indicated the imminent firing of a number of staff and this unfortunate role had earnt him the title, 'the Angel of Death': *L'ange de la Mort.*

There was much whispering in corridors at work because Ron was both black and gay. In 1989 our French colleagues were at times openly chauvinistic and sexist, not to mention homophobic. During my time on reception I had grown accustomed to men's arms slipping around my waist when colleagues popped by reception for a chat, cigarette ash dropping onto my switchboard in the days before strict no-smoking laws were introduced. It was acceptable for *cadres* to give you lung cancer from passive smoking, but *non-cadres* had to retire to the designated smoking zones. It wasn't uncommon for male members of staff to slap a girl's arse. One culprit, with eight grabbing octopus arms, worked in packaging – the official superior to Yazid and Bertrand. His name was René Bonnard. He spent much of his time leaning on reception and sharing his philosophical views of the world with anyone who'd listen, while parking a fat stubby-fingered hand on the closest portion of flesh available. He informed me that a woman from a neighbouring company, a voluptuous blonde lady, impeccably dressed, had come into her own since she had hit forty and that she was now a cherry ripe for the picking. He told me that she was married but that she had had sex over the boot of her colleague's car in level-three parking. The man with whom she had copulated was a stringy looking *cadre* with a handlebar moustache, sprawled over the bonnet of an Alfa Romeo. René had viewed it all on CCTV – as head of security – and was as *au fait* with this woman's sexuality as if he'd held her coat while she'd been in the act.

Sexist comments in the company were rife. Women drivers were scorned and openly told they were at their best in the kitchen or the bedroom, though I had noticed that some men visibly shrank from reception when

Madame Calmelane passed by. She was an exception: the iron lady of the company; the Margaret Thatcher of the enterprise revered because of her salary and her position. The secretarial pool was an easy target for lustful salesmen and there was little respect for administrative staff, much less the receptionists. Lisbeth was considered with little more respect than a prostitute by those that guessed at the nature of her relationship with Mr Charles-Henri Rocheran. The talk was all around the corridors. *It won't last. Only shagging her because his wife left him; his ex was a* cadre, *you know. Marketing manager and top of her game. Brighter than her husband, some say.*

One quiet lunch hour I was engrossed in *Anna Karenina*, when a salesman skidded to a halt in front of reception and said with a look of utter astonishment, 'You read books like *that*?' This wasn't a reproach of my time-wasting activities, rather an expression of surprise that I wasn't filing my nails, applying nail varnish, or reading a magazine for girls. The assumption that receptionists must be stupid was hard to bear. I'd not forgotten my school days and still wanted to aim for the stars. I wondered if I'd moved back to the UK, whether I would have pursued my dream to work in theatre. Would I have settled for working on a switchboard back home?

I scribbled stories in my notepads when no-one was around and sent them off to competitions. I finished a full-length children's book about wizards and witches and wands, and sent the manuscript to a London publisher who, long before the arrival of Harry Potter, wrote back with utter certainty, '*Wands have waved their last.*'

With Ronald McKenzie's arrival, the shockwaves of change were felt on every level, including my own. It was intriguing to watch the agony some members of staff felt they must endure, at having to take orders from a black, English-speaking homosexual. In similar vein to my old headmaster, Ron believed that it was possible to jump rank, challenging the age-old French attitude of 'once a receptionist, always a receptionist'. The winds of change were blowing through the corridors of La Tour Washington.

The concept of a career change was foreign to most of my French colleagues. Academic choices were made by students early on, their future lives mapped out before they were out of *maternelle*. Once a profession had been chosen, it was hard to switch paths. There were a few examples of firemen going back to college and becoming doctors, or typists taking night-school classes and moving up to HR. But these were the exception. If you landed in a rut, that's usually where you stayed. This was the message I was given on a subliminal and literal level day after day, year after year. The French were well-oiled trains, taking their holidays at the same time each year, following the same rules. It was easier and more appreciable to be a sheep than a loose cannon – or worse, an individualist.

Ron's immediate suggestion that I be plucked from the switchboard and put into a position of authority, using my skills in English and working with the head office in Atlanta, was something which was disrespectful of tradition. I was getting 'above my station' – a danger my mother had repeatedly drawn my attention to, and for the first time, Madame Calmelane gave me the cold shoulder.

My friendship with Ron ostracised me from my French colleagues. I was seen to be 'sucking up' to a man in a position of authority. For Ron, it was worse. He was seen to be hanging out with the *riff-raff*. How was it possible that one of the European Headquarter Managers had chosen to become friends with the lowest of the low? A switchboard operator! It broke all the rules in the book and could only be explained by his *Americanness*, his *blackness*, his *gayness*. There wasn't a stream of French people waiting to befriend Ron, and only the English speakers took him into their hearts – a small kernel of foreigners: Jay; a mutinous looking girl named Olivia from Norwich; an Irish girl from Cork called Roisin who had just married a Chinese man; and me of course. Not a single French name to add to the list.

We hung out at Le Knit, a bar at the bottom of the Washington Tower, and drank beer late into the night – none of us keen to go home. René Bonnard joked openly with the other sales guys about how they should 'keep their backs to the wall' if they took the lift at the same time as Ron. I felt protective of him. He spoke little French and was genuinely one of the kindest people I'd ever met. He was an easy target for their jibes, smiling at members of staff all too ready to ridicule him.

Madame Calmelane sent me into town to furnish Ron's vast apartment on the rue de Rennes using company expenses. We sat in Darty the electrical shop and were treated like royalty as we ordered everything Ron needed at one go: fridge, freezer, music system, giant-sized TV. We hung out at his place in the evenings and watched black-and-white movies with Bette Davis, or re-runs of *Dallas* and *Dynasty*. We were both homesick in our own way. When I caught flu Ron let me stay at his palace and tucked me up on his sofa with some broth. We watched a film where a mother told an ailing child that, *if you don't eat your broth, you won't get to see the almond trees in spring*. Ron told me that I was far too thin and that if I didn't eat my broth, I wouldn't get to see no God darn almond trees either.

Ron called me his Lady Di, seeing in my face something of hers. He joked about how I was his *white princess mistress*, and that I should *kick his black ass* back to the kitchen. He told me in deepest Atlanta drawl, that no matter who I dated, and whichever guy I fell for, or moved in with, *a girl needs her own nest-egg*. It's one of the best pieces of advice anyone has ever given me, and one that all women should follow, but I didn't listen. I was young, and I believed that life would sort itself out in the end. There was time around the corner for saving. I was spending my salary as quickly as I earnt it – and although I didn't have any precious eggs, soon I'd have a bird.

CHAPTER 22

One night in Chatelet les Halles, I'd half an hour to spare before meeting Ron for drinks at the Irish pub. The Centre Commercial at the exit to the train station was still open and I fancied buying a new dress to wear for my next date with William. Feeling like a hobbit, I wandered into a labyrinth of underground shops, where there was little hope of sourcing a drop of Vitamin D from the harsh strip lighting above. On the lower level there was a pet store, and before I knew it, I found myself wandering in, lured by the familiar sound of budgerigars chattering in their cages. I'd not been inside more than a minute when I saw a sad-looking parrot who couldn't have been further displaced from the Amazonian rainforests of his home if he tried. The bird looked at me sadly before pecking idly at his own foot to remove the ring from his ankle.

I knew from my budgie-keeping years that this little fellow wasn't happy. Happy birds sit in a puffed-up ball with one leg raised, looking sleepy, or run up and down singing and chattering, whereas this one was long and lean with anxiety. His plumage was dull and the look in his eye hopeless. He edged to the side of the cage as if sensing a kindred spirit. I made the kind of silly reassuring noises I knew birds liked and he responded, bowing his head so that I might scratch his neck through the bars of his cage. The bird was tame but miserable. I wanted to save him, but he came with a whopping price tag of 17,000 francs. But this feathered captive had pulled on my heartstrings. I decided on a plan.

'Alors, *mademoiselle*, you wish to have a loan, *n'est-ce pas?*'

'Yes, please.'

'And how much do you wish to borrow?'

I was sitting in a grand tower block on Le Parvis de la Défense at the head office of La Société Générale, next to the Washington Tower where I worked.

Madame Calmelane had insisted that I open the account when I signed my contract, as my salary was paid directly into it on the 28th of each month.

'17,000 francs, *s'il vous plaît.*'

At the time, this was about £1,700 – almost two months' salary.

'You have a good salary, *mademoiselle*. I suppose you wish to put down a deposit on a house. Perhaps you want to buy an apartment? *Un prêt immobilier?* If so you must wait a little longer, you have not yet been with your company three months. But I am optimistic we can help you with a mortgage in the future.'

'Well, actually, it's not an apartment I want.'

'Ah, a small car perhaps? *Une nouvelle voiture?* This may at least be possible.'

'I can't drive.'

'I see. So, works to your flat then I imagine?' *'Non.* If you will let me explain …'

'We are open to all kinds of projects, *mademoiselle.*' The man sat back in his chair and opened his arms expansively.

'*Allez-y.* Go on.'

'*Je voudrais acheter un perroquet.*'

I had practised my sentence, learning the French word for parrot. I could see that the man did not think he had heard me properly. From his window, there was a clear view across La Défense; an impersonal concrete expanse stretching all the way to the Grande Arche de la Défense and beyond it to Paris itself. Smartly dressed business men and women were walking like determined ants in every direction. There was a sense of purpose here. It was all so cutting-edge. I was no doubt the first person in his career to ask to take out a personal loan to buy a parrot. I was almost certainly the first English woman to do so.

'*Pardon?*' he said at last. '*Un perroquet.*'

A brief silence.

'You want to buy a parrot. *Pourquoi?*'

It was a good question. Why did I want to buy a parrot when I didn't have a flat yet of my own? I couldn't tell him that I had bonded with the bird and been back to see him at least five times; that I had asked the pet shop owner if she would take him out and let him sit on my shoulder. Though it turned out he had a far worse temper than my childhood budgie, who had never once bitten me, and had nearly nipped the top of my finger off not to mention drawing blood from the tip of my ear, I could not bear the fact that he was sitting in an airless glass cage more suited to a guinea pig than a wild bird.

I couldn't tell him this, nor the fact that I had already named him Basil – after Basil Fawlty and his bad temper. I was sure that he wouldn't be so grumpy once I got him home. Nor could I tell the man that my budgie Joey died of a broken heart when I went to university and that I missed him still. I needed to look all determined and grown-up.

'*Je ne sais pas*,' he said cautiously. 'I must ask my manager. Were you not to honour the repayment of the loan, I'm not sure we could repossess a parrot as we might a car. And on my form ...' he looked down at the paper on his desk, 'I'm not sure which box to tick.'

I was learning that to get anywhere in France, you must tick all the boxes. France was an administrative country, and before anything could be achieved, the person sitting in front of you had to tick the right box.

'I'll be in touch,' he said.

A week later I was travelling home with Basil in his cage on the metro. The train pulled into La Défense station on the RER A line from Chatelet. The cage was heavy, and I was wedged between passengers when a homeless man boarded the train. As we lurched forwards the man began to explain that he was hungry and had lost his home and job. I didn't have any money in my purse and I busied myself fussing with Basil as the man passed, too ashamed to look up without being able to offer him something. It was a tough crowd that evening, and no-one dug deep. Angered, the man paced up and down the carriage waiting for the next stop. The train had come to a halt in one of the long tunnels, and we waited, knowing that no explanation would be given by the driver. The man came to a halt beside me and as I looked up he caught my eye. He stared at Basil in disbelief. Angered by the sight of the bird in the cage, he started to shout at the passengers, forcing them to look up from their hardback historical and philosophical novels.

'*Nous sommes tous des prisonniers*. We are all prisoners! Just like this poor bird in its cage. *La pauvre bête.* Trapped behind bars just like you, *Pauvres cons.* You're trapped in your lives. I am trapped in my poverty. The bird is trapped. *Libérez-le*! I say. Free the bird!'

The man grabbed the cage and started to pull at the bars, rattling it and causing Basil to flap manically, letting off a jungle roar that resonated up and down the aisle. I gripped onto the bars, for the love of Basil, and also because I'd not yet paid my first monthly instalment at the bank. The man tried to prise away my fingers and wrenched the door open to free the bird.

'*Envole-toi mon pauvre oiseau*! Fly away! *Echappe-toi*!' 'He was unhappy!' I shouted. 'I'm saving him.'

The struggle continued until two other passengers became embroiled. Finally, the train lurched forwards and minutes later the doors were buzzing open and the man was gone.

I took Basil home to introduce him to William and Lisbeth. He settled in well. We kept the roof of the cage open and he sat on the top, climbing down to run around the floor. He couldn't fly because the pet shop had clipped his wings, but I intended to let them grow back. Soon Basil grew tame and became a part of the family, though never averse to the odd finger-slicing pinch of the beak if we brushed his feathers the wrong way.

It was a couple of weeks before Christmas, and I was in bed at Lisbeth's house one night, with Basil sleeping in his cage. It was a week night, so I was alone while, back at barracks, William had dutifully attended a regimented supper with his parents. Around two o'clock in the morning, I was awoken from a deep sleep by the sound of cries and screams from Lisbeth. I knew that she had spent the evening with Charles-Henri and it was obvious the noises were coming from her bedroom. Lisbeth was a vociferous lover and I stuck my head under my pillow, hoping it wouldn't scare Basil too much. After a moment, it became clear that the cries were not cries of pleasure. There was the sound of a smash and a struggle, and the noise of the window slamming loudly shut and then open several times, as if Lisbeth was trying to push her lover from it. My stomach churned. I hated the sound of arguing, reminiscent as it was of my own parents screaming and shouting. Once again, I was the helpless child who felt somehow guilty, wondering if one was going to knife the other. I was too old by now to hide under the diningroom table and pull the tablecloth down.

God only knew what was happening, but soon the couple were out on the balcony and the screams continued, piercing the frosty night air, silent now the throb of traffic had died down. After a moment the shouting stopped. Charles-Henri must have left. Or died. I didn't know what had fired the argument, the rapid gunshot French was too difficult to understand from afar. Certain that it was none of my business, I rolled over and went back to sleep.

The next morning, I emerged from my room to find Lisbeth drinking tea in the kitchen. She was wearing her white dressing-gown, her face dishwater grey and her hair dishevelled. I smiled, Basil on my shoulder, and asked her if she was alright, wondering if she would confide in me and tell me what all the shouting had been about. She ignored me, stood up, picking up her cigarettes from the table and swept past, her shoulder brushing mine so brusquely that Basil lost his balance.

My flatmate didn't wait for me, but caught an earlier bus to the office, slamming the door on her way out. We barely saw each other that day as Human Resources had relented and she was in training now for her newly upgraded position of secretary. That evening I returned to the house and discovered that my room was freezing cold. Condensation trickled down the window pane. The rest of the house was warm, but my radiator had been switched off. Basil huddled miserably in his cage as the cold air crept in through the windows. When

Lisbeth returned, I asked her if she knew how to fix the radiator, but she shrugged.

'Not my problem,' she said in an unhelpful manner. She continued to cold-shoulder me for several days.

Usually we ate our evening meals together, but she pointedly prepared a microwaved 'meal for one' and shuffled off to her own room to eat it alone. The next morning, I realised that she had removed the hair dryer from the bathroom, presumably because she knew I did not own one, and the television set had vanished from the living room into her bedroom. The temperature outside continued to plummet, and the inside of my window iced up. I moved Basil's cage into the sitting room where it was warmer.

'I don't want that bird in here,' she said, although she had always made a fuss of Basil. I dragged the cage back and started to worry. Basil had sneezed several times and was sitting with his head under his wing which was unusual during the day time. I had noticed that he was moulting and that the bottom of his cage was covered in green feathers.

'Have you asked her what's wrong?' William suggested.

I followed his advice and tried to corner her in the kitchen one morning.

'Have I done something to upset you?' I asked.

'As if you don't know!' she snapped, and then bursting into tears, flounced off to her room.

Within three days the situation had deteriorated. Basil had lost so many feathers that I could see the white duvet that warmed his flesh, lining the bottom of the cage. The room was freezing and his sneezing had become worse and worse. He hadn't touched his food.

'We need to get the heating in my room fixed,' I pleaded. 'I am paying rent after all.'

'I don't want your money,' Lisbeth snapped, her dark eyes lined with black shadows, 'I just want you out. *Salope.*'

I looked up the meaning of *salope*. The closest equivalent in English was 'whore'.

With William's help, I packed Basil into a small cardboard box wrapped with covers and took him back to the pet shop. The man in charge took him from me as efficiently as a doctor in ER.

'He needs medication and to go into the incubator,' he said.

It was a relief they could offer a solution and that they appeared to know exactly what they were doing. I visited Basil in Chatelet les Halles every night after work. Within a few days his feathers had almost completely fallen out, so that he resembled a prisoner of war in his patchy undercoat. The small glass cage pulsated heat, and I wished I could crawl in, rather than return to my freezing damp bedroom.

Ron came with me to visit the patient, and so did William. We did nightly visits and then went for a meal in town, eating our favourite carpaccio and chips *à volonté* in the bistros around the Pompidou Centre. We took Ron to Kitty O'Shea's Irish bar behind the Opéra, where there was live music with an amazing jazz singer much revered by Jessica in the old days. She was called 'Miss Thing' and when she sang I felt as if we were in downtown New Orleans. I returned home as late as I could, drunk if possible, in the hope of avoiding Lisbeth.

Irish bars and American restaurants were big news – all the French *jeunesse* hung out in them. They were fun places to be, with the ambiance of pubs back home. French cafés felt cold in comparison, with impersonal strip lighting more suited to warehouses than places of relaxation, flashing money machines and plastic tables blighting their decor. Old men huddled in the traditional cafés, dropping the butt ends of their cigarettes to the floor. This carpet of cigarettes was a tradition in all French cafés until the no-smoking laws came into practice some years later.

Irish pubs didn't allow cigarettes on the floor. They were warm and cosy, with wooden tables and warm lighting which illuminated dozens of young attractive Frenchmen who were there to chat up the American and Australian tourists, or the English *au pairs*. The wheel had come full circle. I was back where I'd started out with Jessica: working life in the city had taken me away from student haunts such as these, and thrown me into a more adult and grown-up world. I felt a pang of regret that Jessica had left and that she wasn't with me for a drink and some mild flirtation with a stranger before we returned to the comfort and safety of the house of Axel Blanchard.

Running away had seemed a good idea at the time, but then with our strained diplomatic relations with the Chinese, the sudden onset of working life and problems with both money and accommodation, I suddenly longed for the insouciance of those early days, where we raided the fridge when Les Blanchards were in bed and drank cheap wine in the Hessian Sack. I'd have relished an afternoon ironing in the warmth of The Submarine, listening to *Woman's Hour*. The shrill shriek of the switchboard had deprived me of any time for introspection and thought, far more than the ironing of Axel's shirts or the folding of his underpants had ever done.

On the nights when William slept in my room I felt safe again. I didn't like being alone with Lisbeth in the house these days. Her animosity was tangible. She looked as if she might knife me. I still had no idea what I had done.

Since Lisbeth had denied me access to the TV set, I was cut off from what was happening in the world, which increased my sense of isolation. I tried to keep up by buying an English newspaper from La Gare Saint Lazare in the mornings. To escape the ongoing misery of Lisbeth's cold shoulder, I bought books in English from Shakespeare & Company by the Notre Dame, or WH Smith on the rue de Rivoli.

The mystery as to what had happened with Lisbeth was resolved the following week. I was on reception when a Chinese girl from the 24th floor came to the desk. Her name was Ying Yue. She was an attractive woman who spoke extremely good English and French. I had learnt from Lisbeth some time ago that she lived with a

Moroccan man who drank and beat her up. She'd also informed me that Ying Yue was bisexual. She had two children but had had a string of men, and a relationship with one of the female members of staff at the office. She was older than us, in her early thirties perhaps. She cut straight to the point, leaning over the reception desk in a conspiratorial manner. Her voice was soft and raspy with a snake-like undertone.

'You don't know it,' she said, 'but one day you will marry Charles-Henri Rocheran.'

'*Pardon?*' I said, shocked '*Je ne comprends pas*. You must have the wrong person.'

She laughed.

'I told Lisbeth you'd be surprised,' she said 'I see things you can't. Messages from *au-delà*. The other side. You haven't a clue what's going on with Charles-Henri. And Lisbeth thinks you've planned the whole thing. But whatever you think, it will come to pass. You will have a child too. You won't stay with him, but that's for later.'

'*C'est ridicule*,' I said. What total bollocks. The woman was off her head.

Madame Calmelane walked past reception for the third time and glared at me. Ying Yue was part of the influx of staff that had come in with the merger from the enemy company. It was pretty obvious from her look what my boss thought of Ying Yue.

'You don't believe me,' Ying Yue said standing her ground. 'Show me a photo and I'll tell you something.'

The only photograph I had in my purse was one of my mum and dad and my brother Steven. She took it from me and stared at it long and hard.

'Your brother will die young,' she said. 'I forgot to say not to ask me about the future if you don't want to know bad stuff. Oh, and it's possible your dad is not really your dad.'

I snatched the photo back.

'What's this got to do with Lisbeth? What am I meant to have done?'

She smiled, and I thought I didn't like her much, with her sly, knowing looks. Telling me my brother was going to die – how sick was that?

'Lisbeth is obsessed with Charles-Henri,' she said. 'She loves his children and his lifestyle and thinks she will be moving to his big house in the suburbs. He doesn't love her. She is a plaything for sex.'

'How do you know?'

She shrugged. 'I just do. But that's not the point. The other night when you were in bed, they were having sex when Charles-Henri said something that made Lisbeth mad with grief.'

'What?' I asked, pushing back a sudden thought of a demonic Lisbeth wielding a knife.

'He asked Lisbeth if she would go to your room and invite you to join them both in the bed.'

'How do you know?' 'Lisbeth told me.'

'What? He's mad. I would *never* do that.'

She looked at me carefully. 'I know you wouldn't. I think you are a romantic and I think he is in love with you. But you should be careful. Lisbeth wants to kill you. She thinks you encouraged him.'

'I *didn't*! I've never spoken to the man. Whenever I see

him he's always kissing Lisbeth. Anyway, what an insult to think I'd even *want* to go in bed with them. I've got better things to do. I'm going out with William.'

'That won't last,' she said, smugly. 'I tell you, you will marry Charles-Henri and William will sleep with dozens more women after you. I told Lisbeth there is no point killing you or switching the heating off. Did you know she's trying to freeze you out of the house?'

'My parrot is in intensive care!' I said indignantly.

She laughed. 'Look for a new place. Your Lisbeth days are over. Think of me on your wedding day to Charles-Henri.'

She was like the thirteenth fairy. I would need to look out for the pricking needles of a spinning wheel.

'I don't even fancy him! He looks like John Major!' 'You say that now, but one day you will feel differently.' She walked to the door, turning as she got there.

'By the way, I forgot to tell you, Lisbeth tried to jump from the upstairs window that night. Charles-Henri had to pull her back inside. She wanted to kill herself – or rather show the world how angry she was. I'd hurry up and find a new place if I were you.'

I was angry with Ying Yue – angry that she had told me my brother would die, or that my father wasn't biologically related to me. The crap about marrying Charles-Henri was one thing – that was just plain ridiculous – but predicting my brother's early death when he was only seventeen was horrendous. I didn't like her knowing manner, her evil comments or her sneaky smile. The other piece of worrying news was that Lisbeth, who was clearly on the edge of an emotional precipice, had tried to jump out of the window! It explained the banging and shouting. I was so upset that when Henriette Fresnel walked past she noticed the look on my face and invited me into her office. I told her the story. I know I wasn't meant to, and that Lisbeth's relationship was supposed to be a secret, but I was just about to find myself homeless a week before Christmas, Basil was in an incubator but needed to come home at some point, and I was meant to be flying out to Manchester by the end of the week for Christmas. Henriette made a few quick phone calls.

'We might have a solution,' she said. 'It's not the flat you were on the list for, but it's better than nothing, and at least you can move straight away. It's in the Chinese area; the 13th arrondissement.'

I was not too pleased at being back in the heart of the Chinese area, with my old friends lurking nearby, but it was probably the last place they would look for me. Anyway, I was too excited to finally have an address in Paris of my own to care. Basil was finally on the mend and after Christmas I would be able to bring him back to our own place. His feathers had started to push back through; hard, keratin-covered spikes, that made him look more like an emaciated porcupine than a parrot, erupting all over his skinny body. William helped me move. Lisbeth refused to speak to me, slamming doors and chain-smoking in the corner in her trusty white dressing gown. I was furious at Charles-Henri for causing me such grief. The idea that I would even have *wanted* to join him in bed while he was halfway through making love to Lisbeth was sick. I thought of Jay and his sex clubs, feeding coins into machines after work, and Charles-Henri with his *ménage à trois* fantasies, and realised that the real world was far different from that of Mr Darcy and all the other romantic heroes I'd grown up loving. I thought of Madame Blanchard, and her gentleman callers at the house, and Mr Blanchard turning the naked secretary from his room like Eve from the garden of Eden, and decided I'd rather find a husband as faithful as Mr Blanchard, with simple ideas on love, sex and fidelity, than any of the others. Even David, with his pages of looping and flowery prose, hadn't lasted long. First woman in a grass skirt and he'd headed off into the tropical sunset. And William seemed more intent on keeping his parents happy and staying home feasting on veal suppers than spending time with me. Maybe I didn't need a man at all.

Maybe from now on it was just me and my parrot.

CHAPTER 23

Any hopes that William could be the man for me were slowly diminishing. He was either at home obeying his father's iron rule or, even when on leave from barracks at the weekends, devoting large chunks of his free time to a new arrival in our lives: Fabrice. Fabrice – the dreaded best friend – had been away travelling for the first few months of our relationship. But now that he was back our lives were about to take a turn for the worse.

William and Fabrice had been friends since school, and although in many ways were entirely different, especially in their attitude to women, they were inseparable. Fabrice had a face chewed by early bouts of acne, a large, easy smile, tight jeans, a thick leather belt, and pointy black shoes. Worst of all he wore a gold medallion and left the top buttons of his shirt undone, to reveal a golden chain nestled in a thatch of dark hair. It was John Travolta with a hormone imbalance.

I hadn't realised that anyone other than the Bee

Gees actually wore medallions, but Fabrice, like so many Frenchmen, sported both a golden chain and a heavy link bracelet. Jewellery was not the only cultural difference. Since my days with David, I had been initiated over time to the French 'man bag'. Most Frenchmen carried some form of handbag or purse. I wondered where British men kept their keys, driving licence and loose change. I didn't remember my father or any of the other men back home having *a handbag*. French men sported them with ease: little leather shoulder bags, satchels, or purses not unlike the one I carried myself. Fabrice and William were no exception and, not for the first time, I realised that although there was only the English Channel, *La Manche*, to separate us, we were worlds apart.

Due to William's curfew on week nights, our time together began on Friday nights and ended on Sunday afternoons at around four o'clock, allowing William enough time to scamper home in time for the Sunday night aperitif and the passing around of those little bowls of Pringles. I was not invited home on Sunday nights, as William's father told him they all needed to get their heads down for a good night's sleep and work the next day. For the first couple of months of our relationship, before Fabrice's return to Paris, our weekends had been our own and I'd come to terms with the fact that although I didn't see William during the week, he was all mine at the weekend. During the week, I could hang out at Ron's and watch old-fashioned black-and-white movies.

I'd moved out of Lisbeth's house a few days before Christmas. I picked up my key, dumped my stuff at the new studio flat with barely a second glance, and caught a flight home to Manchester, returning to my parents' bungalow for the first time since I'd moved to Paris. Basil was recovering nicely, but was still at the pet shop, in the incubator, in the bowels of Chatelet les Halles commercial centre. Christmas was a relaxing week at home with my parents and brother watching TV – the old favourites: *Only Fools and Horses, Coronation Street, EastEnders*. We drank sherry, and my mother was on her best behaviour, preparing home-made favourites such as mince pies and sherry trifle.

Returning to Paris in the New Year I discovered that Fabrice, the prodigal friend, had pitched up during my absence, following a long voyage to the United States. His return marked the beginning of the end of our relationship. As Lady Diana went on to say only a few years later, 'there were three of us in our marriage'. From that time on, there were three people in our relationship, only one of them should have been on tour with the Bee Gees.

Friday nights, William informed me, were now to be spent at the Queen nightclub on the Champs Elysées *avec* Fabrice, who didn't (*quelle surprise*) have a girlfriend but believed in open relationships with as long and as diverse a cast list as possible. Both before and after the nightclub there were drinks at Fabrice's in the *14ème arrondissement* near the Quai Bercy, and if we were at a loose end, which basically meant if it was just the two of us, William happily informed me that we could meet up with his old friend not only on a *Friday* night, but on a *Saturday* night too. Sunday night William would be back home *chez les parents,* and so the weekend was over before it had begun.

The Queen nightclub was decked out in the late 1980s and early 1990s with the full-sized carcass of a plane wreck which filled the centre stage. Later, the club would become famous in the gay community for its *Soirées Mousse*, where foam was squirted into the audience to hide a multitude of sins. In our day, it was a popular pick-up joint for frustrated heterosexuals like Fabrice. He gyrated around the crash-site, targeting women under every wing. If he 'pulled,' he disappeared off down the runway; if unsuccessful, he trailed us till dawn, cigarette in hand until my throat felt like the bottom of Basil's cage. In a puff of nicotine smoke, William, the gentle and considerate boyfriend I'd learnt to love over the past few months all but vanished.

Fabrice's attitude to women was plain: they were there for sex, and it was okay to have multiple partners without any form of protection. The end of my school days had been marked only a few years before with that chilling advertisement of a chisel carving a gravestone and warning of the dangers of unprotected sex. For Fabrice, AIDS was only something gay men picked up, and he slept with dozens of unknown women across the city without protection. William told me that Fabrice had lost his virginity when they were at boarding school to a woman in her forties, whom he had kept as a mistress for many years, and with whom he still slept when at a loose end. I was surprised he could find one partner, let alone several, but gyratory apes sporting medallions were clearly more in demand than I had reckoned, and the stream of women he could lure back to his apartment never seemed to dry up.

With the return of Fabrice, William's other friends reappeared on the scene. There was Serge, a Corsican artist whose parents had a quirky house with a garden in the centre of town, with an original Picasso sketch in the toilet. Serge's father had been good friends with Picasso who, being, a generous man, had gifted the sketch. Serge was the nicest of William's friends and much higher on the evolutionary scale than Fabrice. Then there was Paul-Edouard, who worked as a consultant for an auditing company, and Hervé, who had shared a flat with William in New York.

William's friends had a closer bond with each other than any of the women they slept with, and suddenly I became the exception, tagging along week after week on 'boys nights out'. In Fabrice's mind, I was a threat. I pitched up at his man-pad on weekends, attending his parties and objecting vociferously to his plans to take my boyfriend to the Club Med in Greece without me. William assumed a different personality around his friend. When he was in 'Fabrice-mode', I wasn't sure I liked him much anymore, and started to wonder who the real William was. English lent a softness to his character that was stripped back in his mother tongue – people become different things around different people, especially in different languages.

Conversations between the men were invariably

about *les nanas* or *le sport*. 'Telephone', a French rock group, blasted away in the background as the men rolled joint after joint and discussed who amongst their latest conquests was hot, and who was not.

Je rêvais d'un autre monde, où la terre serait ronde,' the singer boomed.

All of William's friends smoked, as did the women they brought home on their one-night stands. The fact that I was a non-smoker (pot or otherwise) and a non-drinker (of whisky at least) made it easy for Fabrice to mock me as *ennuyeuse* or boring. I was back in my role as 'Miss Goodie Two Shoes'. Never the 'cool kid' in school, I overheard Fabrice teasing William about the eczema on my hands, jibing his friend for having grown boring now he was shagging 'snakeskin' woman. Our nights together ended with me in the corner, disapproving and longing to go home.

Back in the 13th, at my flat, we made love, waking late into the next day when it was already afternoon. Sundays were the worst. When I was young my father had worked away from home and left the house on Sunday afternoons at four, timing his departure with the start of my favourite television programme: Black Beauty. Week after week I would watch that most magnificent of all horses galloping over the hillside, the dramatic theme tune punctuating my sobs. I dreaded the time the clock would chime four, just as now I found myself dreading the exact same time William would leave. Sunday afternoons became a symbol of sadness in my week, the depression lifting by Monday when I was back at work with Ron, or out drinking after work with the Brown & McLane Software team. But on Sunday afternoons, as the curtains closed on our window of opportunity, I couldn't enjoy our time together, knowing the minutes were counted.

'Why don't you stay one more night? It won't matter.' 'I don't have my work clothes.'

'Let's go and get them.'

'Let's make love again instead. It's too far to drive and my parents will want us to stay for dinner – and it will be awkward. My mother won't have prepared enough portions.'

'Bring your clothes to mine next week. Let's spend a whole week together. I want to know what it's like to be with you on a Wednesday!'

'We're fine as we are, aren't we? We'll be tired in the week from work. This way, we just spend the nice moments together. Besides, I told you, my parents won't like it.'

What was wrong with his parents! I'd seen my own just a handful of times in the last couple of years. William was an adult for god's sake. When was he going to stand up to them and live his own life?

With Fabrice's return, I learnt secrets from William's past that I didn't like at all. Fabrice, sprawled back in his chair, cigarette drooping from his slack mouth, greasy locks of hair falling onto his brow, let these nuggets of information fall one by one, relishing the moment.

'Remember that night you and Hervé shagged the same girl?'

I wasn't sure I'd heard properly. *What*? There was more.

'*Ouaiii, C'était très con.* Stupid, you know. Years ago, now.

This girl, she couldn't choose, so we both fucked her.'
'On the same night?'

Fabrice laughed. 'At the same time, more like!' 'For fuck's sake!'

'Well, darling,' William said, trying to slip his arm around my waist, 'it was not a happy experience. Not one of which I'm proud.'

It was repulsive. These actions were so far removed from my idea of love that I pushed William away. I didn't know anyone at university who had done that. Not even the rugby lot, or the porn brigade from the Ifor Evans TV room. There were the drinking games, and the Welsh boys joking that they were going out '*on the tap*', but there was also a notion of falling in love, of being in love, of wanting to be with that special person – even if they did puke all over her.

'*C'est dégoutant!* I feel sick!' 'Thanks! I wish I'd never told you.'

Later that night: 'Do you want to sleep with every woman you see?'

'I'm with you, aren't I?' 'Do you love me?'

There was a pause.

I blurted out without thinking: 'Would you live with me? We could get a nice place together. With Basil. On both our salaries we could afford a gorgeous two-roomed flat, or a duplex apartment. Saint Michel perhaps. Or Le Marais.'

This time the answer was loud and clear.

'No. I've decided to rent an apartment with Fabrice.'

Part of my desire to live with William stemmed from the loneliness I felt now that I had moved into my new studio. The apartment was 27m² and in a block of HLM (or Council) flats in the rue Domrémy in the *13ème arrondissement*. It was located near the new Paris library which was under construction but as yet a wasteland. A cold wind blew down the rue Domrémy and when Ron and Olivia, his colleague from work, popped over, they soon baptised my street the 'Wind Tunnel'. The flat was on the third floor, next to the lift. I would have preferred an older more Parisian feeling flat, such as the one provided by Magwitch our Chinese benefactor, but the innocuous and soulless decor was a small price to pay for keeping all my fingers.

The door opened onto a small corridor with a shower-room and a toilet, and one room with a corner-kitchen fitted out with an electric hotplate. There wasn't a fridge, so I put my milk on the window sill. The idea of popping out to an electrical goods store such as Darty never occurred to me. Finances were tough with my monthly direct debit for Basil. Basil's open cage took up most of the main sitting room. I placed my faithful camp bed beneath the window, to serve both as a place to sleep and a place to sit during the day. There was a fitted cupboard in the entrance hall for my clothes, but I didn't have a table or a chair; so most of my belongings lay scattered on the bird-seed covered floor. Compared to the flat I'd shared with Jessica, it was dire. The Eiffel Tower and the Sacre Coeur felt like fairy-tale myths up here. And yet, however dreary it was, this was the first place I could truly call home.

It wasn't the sort of flat that Jessica would have dreamt of. It was a concrete box with a carpet floor. There were no old parquet floorboards to creak beneath my feet or cornicing on the ceiling to lift the sprit. It was a functional box in which to eat and sleep, fulfilling the old Parisian doctrine of *métro, boulot, dodo* (metro, work, bed). The flat made no allowance for aesthetics but was the sum of all I could afford.

It was a cold winter, so I hung a plastic bag from my window to store my butter, cheese, and milk. I heated water in the only pan I owned, which served as a kettle and a utensil to cook spaghetti. I couldn't make tea and spaghetti at the same time, so I boiled the water for the tea first and then made the pasta, covering it with ready-made tomato sauce from a jar. The makeshift fridge worked quite well, until I was woken one morning to the sound of cooing, and a fat Parisian pigeon pecking at the lid of my milk and feasting on my cheese. From then on, the word spread across the rooftops of Paris that *l'anglaise* on la rue Domrémy was crazy enough to keep her food outside, so I resigned myself to pecked packets of Emmental cheese, or perforated milk-tops on my fresh milk.

When Basil was released from incubation, he screeched at the pigeons from the top of his cage and relished the council-heated warmth of our tiny new box. I left the door of the cage open and he ran around on the carpet, leaving bird poo everywhere. I was glad of his company and even more pleased when William found me a second-hand TV set. He was endeavouring to creep back into favour, realising how disappointed I was that he'd decided to move in with Fabrice.

François Mitterand was President and there was talk of phase two of the Gulf war and increased conflict. Not to mention Scud missiles landing on France and fear in the city. I started to think that if there was going to be a world war, I'd rather be back in England. I made some comment about this during my weekly phone call, but both my parents reassured me that I was best off where I was, despite being geographically closer to Iraq. A week home at Christmas was one thing; moving back for good quite another.

Mitterand sat behind his grand presidential desk and made a special news announcement in which he told his country that the situation was growing worse. He comforted his fellow patriots and I felt reassured. With talk of war I was more relieved than ever that I resisted the temptation of selling my passport to Yazid.

Madame Calmelane warned us that as a prominent American company we must be even more careful of suspect packages. One such packet arrived at my desk without a label. I called security and the whole tower block was evacuated. A thousand employees stood on the Le Parvis de la Défense in the biting cold wondering if there was to be a controlled explosion of the box. It turned out to be computer software from Provence, returned by a disgruntled client who'd lost his marker pen.

I remembered David's tales of terrorist attacks in Paris and grew nervous on the RER A line at rush hour. The train was packed with hundreds of commuters and there was barely space to breathe. The screeching doors pressed against heaving bodies to close. One morning I uttered a scream which filled the whole carriage, when a man lucky enough to have a seat remained standing, ceremoniously removing a device with a wire from his breast pocket. I realised a second too late that it was his Walkman.

With money so tight, I skipped dinner whenever I could, filling up on beer at *Le Knit* after work. Cooking at the flat was too depressing to eat home every night. I made up for poor diet at the weekend when William took me out for *moules frites* or *carpaccio de boeuf à volonté* in the bistros around St Germain-des-Près where I could stuff my face with third or fourth helpings all for the same price. Basil was a different matter, requiring maximum vitamins after his recent illness. I bought apples from the Arab shop to make sure he had his daily dose.

After a time, my fears subsided. Not a single Scud missile had landed on Paris, and after the air strikes in early January of that year, the war appeared to be over before it had begun. I began to relax.

Spring was in the air and the promise of May in Paris filled my heart with joy. The thought of cherry-tree blossom and afternoons in Les Tuileries, reading a book on a bench and eating a crèpe, sent a ripple of joy through my heart. It had been a long winter. The best thing that could be said about my new studio was that Basil was warm. Our Siberian days at Lisbeth's were behind us, and I'd no reason to complain. Ron, who was a passionate collector of art, promised me he would lend me '*one of his pieces*' to brighten my place up. But when he came over for the first time he stared at the blank walls as if he might cry, and did not renew the offer.

'Come to my place, doll-face,' he said. 'If ever you're down, just pop on over to la rue de Rennes.'

But Ron was busy these days. He was 'courting' a wealthy German (married unfortunately) and his thoughts were elsewhere. Besides, I couldn't leave Basil alone every night. I wondered why I'd tied myself down with a parrot. I'd wanted to rescue him, but it was more than that: I needed someone to love, someone with whom to form a family unit. I wanted a place to call home and someone in it who loved me, even if that someone was an Amazonian parrot.

Returning home one day, I noticed that Basil's apple had turned prematurely black. It was strange. I had only put it out that morning: fresh, hard and green. Every day before work I would pierce an apple between the bars of the cage, leaving his roof top open, so that he could climb up and amuse himself by shredding it to pieces and hurling clumps across the carpet.

I reached out to remove the apple, and froze. It wasn't black. It was covered in cockroaches. My love of animals did not extend to roaches. Basil's apple was covered with fifteen prize specimens, their shining backs gleaming in my face as if to say, 'Go on, *salope*, I dare you. Squish me'.

The problem grew worse over the following days. I

bought poison and traps, leaving them in the corner of the sitting room while I was out at work. Hopeful that these would have done the trick, I turned down the covers of my bed that night, to discover the mother of all cockroaches nestling between my sheets. Shower times were hazardous. Water leaked from the miniscule shower-tray when I washed, sweeping the traps from the corner of the bathroom, and filling them with water, so that dead cockroaches bubbled to the surface in a pool of frothy water.

Each night, on my return, I inspected the flat from top to bottom. It didn't take long. I crossed the floor on tiptoes, with the trepidation of a bomb-disposal officer. There was a fresh cull of victims each day, with new live trails of survivor beasts crawling along the walls. I killed so many it astounded me that they had time to breed. Was my camp bed surrounded by mating roaches each night as I slept; shagging the night away to ensure new growth spurts to the population?

One night, I switched on the eight o'clock news, to ascertain the state of the world and to hear the latest update from our President (*'Mesdames, Messieurs, bonsoir,'*), but was distracted by a line of cockroaches emerging in single file from behind the TV set. They had bedded down in the back amidst the wires, to the comforting warmth of François Mitterrand's words.

My colleague Olivia, who had grown friendlier towards me in recent weeks, offered to repaper my studio flat. She was good at DIY and thought it might help cheer the place up. I saw Ron's sceptical look but thought it was worth a shot. Olivia came over with a steamer to lift coarse sheets of flecked paper from institutional walls. As the steamer started to hiss, the glue on the back of the paper began to melt. She lifted away the first soggy strip which came off in one entire piece. Behind the paper the wall was studded with cockroaches. We continued to work along the wall behind my bed. Living, crawling and breathing in this airless space, were hundreds more mating couples.

I dreamt of cockroaches. In one nightmare, I turned back the sheets to my camp bed poised with a spray can of poison in my hand. The cockroach was waiting but had grown to the size of a plump poodle. It had huge globules for eyes and hissed in anger as I interrupted its siesta. I sprayed clouds of toxic fumes, but it laughed in my face and refused to die.

CHAPTER 24

Opposite my block of flats there was a run of scruffy shops and a Chinese restaurant. We were close to the Place Jeanne d'Arc, and the main hub of the *13ème arrondissement*, but la rue Domrémy was a neglected backwater. I was confident I wouldn't bump into Magwitch, so I popped down to eat at the restaurant on nights when I could no longer face pasta on the four-ring electric hotplate. The infestations inside the flat and the pigeon-pecked food on the window sill had put me off home-made meals for a time. Like Magwitch's old place, the restaurant also had an electronic painting of a waterfall, lit from behind, which cascaded down towards me. Reminders of where I'd seen such a tableau before encouraged a paranoid glance at my waiter's shoes as I verified the height of his heels. Thankfully these were flat.

I drank sake with Olivia and Ron, who always found polite excuses not to come indoors.

As the days grew lighter and longer, and in search of the real Paris, I took the number 27 bus home from the Opéra. It offered one of the best rides in Paris, travelling down past Le Palais Royal, Le Musée du Louvre, and over Le Pont du Carrousel to the *6ème arrondissement* and down to the entrance of Les Jardins du Luxembourg. I strolled in the park by the Palais du Luxembourg and around the ornamental lake before catching the bus home, back to La Place Jeanne d'Arc. The weeknights were lonely and I missed Jessica and our debriefs on the funny events of our day. There was no longer a devil-may-care attitude to life.

Carpe diem had been replaced by a deep-seated worry that this was as good as it got. That this was my new 'grownup life' with its bills and work responsibilities.

The Paris of my dreams could only be grabbed outside working hours, or far from the flat and its scrabbling, drowning, dying, breeding roaches. I snatched it at odd moments, when the last golden rays of light fell onto a couple who kissed on a park bench, as children laughed and played in their smart old-fashioned clothes, rushing past on tricycles like characters straight out of a Robert Doisneau photograph. But this old vision of Paris had become a cliché, something just out of my reach. Real life was the crowded metro in the morning, when there was no time to take the bus because I'd made myself late de-infesting glossy brown corpses from my shower cubicle before I could wash. Life in Paris was hampered by the regular train strikes organised by the RATP when crowds heaved and fought to squeeze between the metro doors. Real life was the one thousand calls a day I put through on my switchboard. If I said 'Good morning, please hold the line, I'm putting you through!' one more time I would go mad. I knew that however challenging it was to answer the phone in French, I didn't want to be a receptionist for the rest of my life. To quote the title of that Marilyn film, *Something's got to give.*

My situation at work was growing complicated. Ron, who meant well, had decided to take up my case, embarking once more on the task of getting me promoted, come hell or high water, which sent Madame Calmelane into a rage.

'Hell doll-face, I don't get these people,' he said. 'Here you are, a degree, fluent in English – in what is, after all, an *American* company – an intelligent mind ... and they don't offer anything better that switchboard operator. Come on, girl! I want you on my team. I've been pussyfooting round this issue for months now.'

Ron went to see Madame Calmelane and told her he wanted me as his PA. Madame Calmelane refused. She had recruited me, and she was keeping me, whether she still wanted me or not. It was a matter of principle. I had not been hired to speak English; I'd been hired to answer the phone in French. I was hers. Lisbeth was now in the secretarial pool and a new girl named Luna had been recruited to replace her but could not be left alone. The answer was no, whether Ron was Head of Human Resources worldwide, or not. If he wanted me, it was war. And if there was war, he'd have to fire Madame Calmelane. Even Ron flailed at this idea.

Our new receptionist, Luna, had a cloud of blonde hair,

huge eyes, full lips, a stunning figure and a mind devoid of interest in anything except fashion. If she had been a character in a novel she would have been a cliché. She filed her nails, as was expected of a receptionist, and painted them, ignoring the shrill cry of the switchboard as they dried. She was a heavy smoker and called me from the 24th floor at regular intervals to tell me '*Je vais fumer ma clope.*' '*Clope*' was one of those slang words the French loved: *clope* for *cigarette*, *boulot* for *work*, *godasses* for *shoes*, *bagnole* for car – replacement words which formed a second language of *argot*, or familiar everyday speech, which I had to learn alongside correct French if I was to understand what was being said. Spoken French was so different from what I'd learnt at school.

Ron was adamant that, with the arrival of Luna, he could promote me into the American branch of his office. A compromise was reached in which I was allowed to assist the Atlanta-based team that was moving to France, while continuing to work for Madame Calmelane. Ron asked me to write a guide in English for expats moving to Paris from the US and I was allowed official writing time every day on my Apple Mac. It was a godsend finally knowing how to use a computer. I continued to type up my stories in my free time, fantasising that maybe one day I could write something good enough to be published, allowing me to unplug my switchboard for good!

Now that I had fallen from grace with Madame Calmelane my days felt numbered. Those cosy trips to the fancy boutiques at the shopping mall were long gone, and my two special work suits were starting to look a little grey and bobbled around the cuffs. There was talk of Ron moving to Brussels within a year, and I realised that if he 'grabbed skirt' and headed out of town without me, my position in the company might no longer be tenable. But if I couldn't go home, what else could I do?

I started to pick up the FUSAC, a freebie magazine in English, advertising jobs and courses, to see what else was available in the city. I also wondered what other parts of France had to offer, amusing myself by looking at adverts in the PAP magazine for stone manor houses at ridiculously low prices in remote regions of France. Further South than Château de Trémouillet, that was for sure. I knew the perils of falling into the belly button of France, and not descending any lower than the Loire valley, which the French always claimed was the demarcation point on the map for sunny weather.

I wanted to escape. I didn't know where or how, but I poured over the adverts until the ink was smudgy; dreaming of farms that were half-dilapidated but full of promise, large plots of land, and even vineyards! Some of them advertised for less than the price of a smart new family car. If I couldn't go home, perhaps I could go somewhere else. Somewhere cheaper, where I didn't have to share a $27m^2$ room with an infestation of cockroaches; a place with a garden for Basil. A home of my own.

The magazine was addictive, and I realised that in the South West of France, in particular, it was possible to buy a sizeable estate with several hectares of land for a pittance.

Many evenings, long after hometime when I'd unplugged my switchboard, I sat perched up high on the 31st floor of La Tour Washington, as the turbaned cleaners wheeled their trolleys into the office, and my colleagues called goodnight as they headed home, my head filled with visions of *maisons de maître*, orchards and hectares of land. Sometimes, by the time I'd got to the end of my journal, it was so late that the lights across Paris had flickered on. I'd been busy in sunlit Provence, decorating old walls with lime plaster and pruning back wisteria. My dream was a stone house, nestling in the southern sunshine, surrounded by woods and trees, with a river at the bottom of the garden. I wouldn't know a soul and I'd be totally alone, at the start of a new adventure – just me and Basil. Strangely, despite the loneliness I felt in Paris, I did not imagine anyone else in my isolated farmhouse. Where was William in this fantasy? Why was he not there with me in Gascony or Provence?

It was June, and William and I had been invited to a party. Fabrice was in tow. The evening was balmy, and Fabrice's shirt was unbuttoned, his medallion twinkling in the sunlight through a nest of hair. We were invited by a friend of a friend to an unknown house in Paris. Our journey led us to a smart house in the western suburbs of Paris, a flight of white stone steps leading to a grand doorway. Standing at the open door were two gorgeous French girls in their midtwenties. These were the type of girls that always made me anxious I might not be enough for William. After all, he couldn't be *that* keen on me. He didn't want to live with me and was flat-hunting with Fabrice. How much clearer a message could he send than this? Fabrice was, after all, the man repudiated to have once wiped his own arse with his girlfriend's towel because he couldn't find any toilet paper. Was he really a better bet than me?

The girls fluttered at the door in pale-green and pink dresses, their long dark hair blowing in the evening breeze. All the French girls I knew had long dark hair and slender figures. I was slim, for I barely weighed seven stone due to lack of food in the week, but I'd had my naturally blonde hair cropped short like a boy. Jessica had always promised that short hair would suit me and show off that long, Modigliani-style neck she claimed I'd inherited—but faced with these two giggling long-haired girls tossing their manes, I wondered if in comparison I didn't look *butch*.

William and Fabrice embraced the girls as if they'd known each other all their lives. French girls were rarely friendly to an unknown woman in a skimpy dress, and they eyed me up and down, briefly proffering cold makeup clad cheeks before turning back to the men. It was the old lift scene back at work. There were men on the radar, so naturally the two alpha males were shunted into the limelight, and the girls grew flighty around them.

One girl had draped herself around William's neck. '*Comment ça va? Depuis le temps?*' she quivered.

It was an odd thing to ask, considering they'd never met. Why would she ask how he'd been keeping? William hadn't mentioned her before.

'You know each other?' I asked, not sure I wanted the answer.

'Mais oui,' she tittered, before William could reply, 'on s'est rencontré mercredi.'

They had met the previous Wednesday. *Wednesday* was a weeknight and thus a night when William should have been home playing the role of dutiful son and eating his plate of sloppy veal out in the suburbs with *Maman* and *Papa*. Clearly not what a twenty-seven-year-old man worth his salt did during the week when there was a perfectly good party in the offing. Perhaps his parents had never demanded he stayed home. It was possible that Fabrice and William had been gadding about town for months now, meeting girls like this and sleeping with them for all I knew. How naive and idiotic could I have been?

To think that last Wednesday night, while I'd sat home alone, William had been here! In this house! With this long-haired flirtatious siren! No wonder she was hanging round his neck like a bauble on a Christmas tree. For all I knew they may already have slept together. With Fabrice watching. Participating! Who was this man I was dating? I was beyond anger. I pushed past and fought my way into the house in search of a drink.

The party resembled any of a thousand others held in and around Paris that night. All the French women smoked, their hands conveniently occupied with this easy accessory. The men rolled joints or picked at the buffet table. Once again, I was the exception – the English girl who couldn't say much and understood even less. The usual English tracks were playing: Fine Young Cannibals 'She drives me crazy', REM's 'Losing my Religion', and by the time I'd stopped crying, Simply Red's 'If you don't know me by now'.

There was a table laden high with bottles of drink and food. The French managed a sense of etiquette even at a student party. Unlike in the UK, it was normal practice not to get blathered and then throw up over the balcony, but to hold one's liquor and to eat a decent meal too. There was potato salad, rice salad, tomato salad, trays of charcuterie, and home-made quiche, made by the girl currently whispering into William's ear, whose parents owned the house. We were the only guests not to have brought a chocolate cake *fait maison* or a savoury dish. It was as if each of these girls was trying to lay out her stake and prove what a fabulous housewife she would make one day. They fussed with napkins and cleared away empty dishes, rifling the cupboards for the right dessert dish. I'd never seen a French student throw up, although they all drank, and smoked weed. It was because of all this endless preparation of food. And because they were careful never to binge drink on an empty stomach. It was also a given that they all drove home on the *Périphérique* afterwards at 100 kilometres an hour. No-one seemed to worry about drink-driving.

Depeche Mode were playing now, the volume to 'Personal Jesus' cranked up. Fabrice was dancing in the centre of the floor, opening the buttons of his shirt as he limboed around a shrieking girl. I couldn't tell what anyone was saying, the music was so loud, and anyway, no-one bothered to talk to me. I was William's girlfriend, so the other men couldn't flirt according to etiquette, and the girls were not interested in a moody English woman in the corner with a sulky face and shorn locks.

I glared at William as the girl with the long dark hair brought him a plastic plate of quiche and salad and fussed around him as if she'd personally puffed the air into the pastry for him. I might as well not have been in the room.

'You didn't say you came here on Wednesday,' I said, as soon as we were alone.

'*Quoi? Je n'entends pas.* The music is too loud. Speak up.'

'YOU DIDN'T SAY YOU CAME TO A PARTY HERE ON WEDNESDAY.'

He shrugged and carried on eating. 'Sorry, I forgot.'

'Why wasn't I invited? I could have come. I was on my own.'

'There wasn't time. Fabrice called. Last-minute thing.'

It was then I knew for certain we had reached the end of our journey. It was over between us. It had been a strange first year, coming to Paris in search of one love, and then thinking I had found another, only to realise with certainty that whatever the future in Paris held for me, I was to face it alone.

EPJLOGUE

The next morning is our last. I will next see William over twenty-one years later at a party in Gascony. He will travel from Lyon where he is living and not knowing what to say to one another, we will stand on my doorstep and kiss as if the years have not crept between us. By this time William will be a shadow of his former self, and that evening, I will learn why. We will speak of the years in between, sipping wine, in a stone house overlooking the Pyrenees; in a room filled with the friends I have made over those long and intervening years.

Until this time we will live out our twenties and our thirties apart and marry different partners. I will become a mother myself, and William will discover that, despite our often-careless and un-protected love-making, the reason I have never fallen pregnant, is because he is unable to have children at all.

By that time it will no longer be possible for him to meet my father or my brother.

But we guess at none of these future heartaches or joys, as we wake that last Sunday morning, snatching our milk from the beaks of pigeons; boiling water in the only pan I own, and checking the cups for roaches.

I am still upset about William's Wednesday escapade to a party without me.

More than this, there is the ring of disappointment that he has not once told me he loves me. With these words I might have been able to forgive him, choosing to believe that the party was a one-off; or accepted his wish to live with his friend, knowing that one day there might be some hope for our relationship.

But on that last morning together he talks of his week and says all the many things it is possible to say to a lover over coffee, when you are determined not to mention the word love.

After breakfast, he takes me into his arms and kisses me. Twenty-one years later I will learn that this is the moment when he will first suspect his true feelings, but I am far from guessing the truth. In my mind I've flown away; drawn a line through him and crossed him out.

We make love on the camp bed, and then, because of its bone-snapping habit of folding in two at inappropriate moments, we pull down the quilt and slip to the floor, falling onto a carpet of sunflower seeds.

When the knock at the door sounds, we are in a still and contemplative hiatus.

There are never visitors to my house on a Sunday morning. It is our precious time together.

None of my friends would call so unexpectedly.

William jumps up and drags on his clothes.

It's Fabrice.

'He wants to know if I can come out to play squash.' I smile. I'm not even angry.

William hunts for his wallet and keys, we agree to meet later that evening.

We are invited to eat curry at the house of an American called Joyce. Olivia will be there, and for once, William has agreed to join us. Although it is a Sunday night.

'*A ce soir.*'

'See you at eight. 27, rue Guénigaud. Don't be late.'

He will not come, and I will end our relationship in anger; a whisper in my heart telling me that there are new lives waiting for me somewhere over the slate-grey rooftops of Paris.

But one day, we will meet again.

About the author

Karen graduated from Aberystwyth University with a Degree in English Literature. She then moved to Paris, where she worked for 16 years as an English language teacher for business professionals before settling in rural South West France. With few employment opportunities other than stuffing geese or picking melons, she qualified as a licensed real estate agent.

Karen then attended Lancaster University where she graduated with a Masters in Creative Writing in 2015, after which she set up a series of Creative Writing retreats, "A Chapter Away", inviting world famous authors, literary agents and publishers to teach aspiring novelists. Inspired by the comments of tutors on the memoir writing course, she began "A Stranger in Paris."

Passionate about theatre, and script-writing, Karen has also written plays, several short stories and a novel – all of which are lurking in the bottom drawer. "A Stranger in Paris" is her first published work, and is the first novel of the trilogy La Vie Française.

Karen now lives in Gascony with her husband and son, and has a grown-up daughter who works in London. Much of her writing is inspired by the North West of England where she grew up, and France which became her country of adoption.